NHS PLEASE DON'T KILL ME!

YOUR SURVIVAL GUIDE TO NHS CARE

DR RAY RADFORD

AND

SCOTTY JOHNSON

Matador
9 Priory Business Park,
Wistow Road, Kibworth Beauchamp,
Leicestershire. LE8 0RX
Tel: 0116 279 2299
Email: books@troubador.co.uk
Web: www.troubador.co.uk/matador
Twitter: @matadorbooks

ISBN 978 1784622 015

British Library Cataloguing in Publication Data.
A catalogue record for this book is available from the British Library.

Printed and bound by CPI Group (UK) Ltd, Croydon, CR0 4YY
Typeset in 11pt Aldine401 BT Roman by Troubador Publishing Ltd, Leicester, UK

Matador is an imprint of Troubador Publishing Ltd

We hope this book helps you and your family in both good and difficult times. We believe it will help us all to change healthcare culture for the benefit of everyone by developing and raising awareness of how better communication skills can influence the care you receive.

DISCLAIMER

This is NOT a medical textbook, and should NOT be used as one.

We, the authors and publishers, accept no responsibility for actions taken or not taken in relation to any medical problem or any action as a result of reading this book. This book offers guidance and tips but is not in itself a medical manual.

Always seek professional medical advice and help if you feel unwell.

CONTENTS

OUR AIMS AND WHY WE HAVE WRITTEN THIS BOOK

We have written this book because we believe that you have the right to the best care possible from the NHS when you need it.

This book is aimed at helping you and your family get the care you all expect and deserve.

You will gain an insight into the world of the NHS, how it often works so well, why things go wrong and how to take responsibility to prevent harm happening to you.

You will learn some essential life and social skills. These skills will show you how to get the best out of the people caring for you, by helping and guiding them to help you.

The purpose of this book is:

* To give you control over your body.
* To help you take responsibility for your own wellbeing.
* To ensure that you are confident that the treatment you get is what is best for you.
* To reduce the risk of something important being missed.
* To help to reduce and remove the risk of you being harmed.
* To give you the skills and knowledge you need to help you make informed decisions.

We aim to help influence in a positive way, your own and your family's care, whilst helping to set a culture that benefits everyone.

We also hope that *every* health professional, *every* hospital manager and *every* politician reads this book and as a result is personally motivated to take positive action to genuinely influence better patient care.

A dream outcome would be that every health professional, whether in a patient-facing role or not, also learns and practises the skills in this book to improve the chances of top class care for every patient they have the privilege and responsibility to care for.

It is now widely acknowledged that for the NHS to improve, patients have to play their part in being better at being able to help the healthcare professional do their job to the best of their ability.

ACKNOWLEDGEMENTS

To all the patients we have met, cared for and shared stories with, every conversation has been an opportunity to learn from you. Sometimes we were inspired by the stories we heard and sometimes we were appalled by how you were mistreated, misdiagnosed and lied to. On each occasion, through asking questions, listening and reflecting, we developed an increased awareness of the current reality of the NHS which helped us to structure this book. Thank you for your **honesty**, **transparency** and **humility**. Ironically, these are the three qualities which we need every person working within the NHS, from politician to porter, to live and breathe every moment, of every day.

– To Julie Bailey of **Cure the NHS** for her encouragement, her leadership and her tenacity in seeking the truth and positive change in the face of extreme adversity and even harassment.

From co-author Ray – a consultant surgeon's view:

"*To all my great teachers in medicine who have patiently taught me, encouraged me and given me the skills to make a positive difference to the lives of tens of thousands of patients, you know who you are. Thank you.*

To the shameless and incompetent colleagues and NHS managers who have caused me illness, grief and frustration, but for who in their avoidance of accountability and responsibility drove me to the positive response of co-authoring this book in the hope that things can change and get better for patients. Some of you know who you are, some of you are still too deluded to realise you are one of them.

We do not have to accept 'we are where we are'. Many people are better than that. Sick, vulnerable people deserve the best possible care from gifted people who do care."

INTRODUCTION

Becoming ill is a fact of life for many of us. Our bodies have developed amazing abilities to fight infection, repair damage from trauma and even prevent cancer. However, sometimes our natural ability to heal is overcome and we need help. When illness becomes too much for our natural defences, we feel a loss of control and we all make the hopeful assumption that our NHS will come to the rescue and care for us to a high standard, in a professional and thorough way.

That assumption, however, has been sadly tarnished by the repeated and on-going reports of inadequate levels of care across the NHS and specifically from the shocking revelations at Mid-Staffs Hospital where there may have been up to 1,200 'unnecessary' deaths caused by a combination of incompetence, lies, denial, professional negligence, avoidance of responsibility, cover-ups, delusion and poor systems.

'Behavioural inadequacy' by staff was something that featured highly in the review of what went wrong at Mid-Staffs Hospital by Robert Francis QC, published in February 2013.

Following numerous enquiries and other revelations, it is heartbreaking to learn that Mid-Staffs was not a one-off. At the time of writing, the media is full of words like *'cover-up'* and *'scandal'* as more and more cases of wilful neglect, harm and fraudulent behaviour are unearthed in other hospitals and care settings. Ann Clwyd MP in 2013 reviewed shocking stories of poor patient care and a pitiless complaints procedure in the NHS that further highlights the need to learn and practise the skills this book will cover.

Healthcare, like any business, could have all the best systems, policies, funding, equipment and technology in the world, but what makes it function or not is the way that individuals use and interact with those systems, with each other, and with the end user – which, in the case of healthcare, is YOU, the patient.

Many healthcare professionals are wonderful, hard working and committed people who do a great job in spite of the system, not because of it. Mistakes and errors happen for many reasons, but what can YOU actually do to detect 'behavioural inadequacy' and avoid being an unfortunate statistic?

It is apparent that within the NHS and even within each individual hospital or healthcare centre, there are vastly differing cultures and levels of care available. As a patient, how are you to know what level of care you are going to get from that trusted person in front of you?

It would be very easy to write pages upon pages of commentary on what is wrong with the NHS – the newspapers are full of it every day. It would also be easy to author a view of the NHS through rose tinted spectacles and pretend that everything is ok really. What we try to do in this book is paint a realistic picture of what actually happens, and how you can take positive steps to help yourself.

'Never events' are the sometimes horrific events that actually happen to patients that should **never** happen – but do. Examples include having the wrong leg amputated, a piece of surgical equipment left inside your body, being given the wrong dose of drugs, and being listed to have both testicles removed when only one had a problem. If you are diligent about learning and practising the communication skills in this book, you will greatly reduce the chances of a 'never event' happening to you. If all healthcare staff were equally as pro-active in their application of effective communication skills, the chances would be even more greatly reduced.

We aim to equip you with the skills and knowledge for you to be in control – of you.

After you have tried using the skills and frameworks in the book, please share your experiences and success stories via our website so that others can learn from you: www.NHSSurvivalSkills.uk

CHAPTER 1

How to use this Book – Your Guide

The aim of this book is to help you get the best care possible if and when you have to use the NHS. We have designed the book to take you through a process of understanding some of the main issues that affect the quality of care you receive, to learning about and developing the skills that will help you address those issues and on to the various parts of your typical 'health journey'; from thinking you may be unwell at home, to seeing your GP and potentially a hospital visit.

Along that journey you will have many conversations. It is these conversations in which you can have a high degree of influence on what happens to you. At each stage of the journey there are key questions to ask and decisions to be made. This book will help you stay more in control of your experience by giving you the relevant skills and knowledge to have the right conversations in order to make the best decisions – for you.

The **Human Factors** section of the book will give you specific insight and the background into why errors, harm and 'never events' frequently happen by looking at the influences of healthcare workers' behaviour. If you have more awareness of why things happen, you can do more to prevent harm happening to you.

The **Communication Skills** section will teach you how to have a quality conversation with meaning and structure. Learning and practising these skills will help you address the issues we highlight in the 'Human Factors' section so you can use them to your benefit during your health journey.

In **Your Health Journey** we take you through the various stages of what typically happens when you fall ill. Whilst we don't cover every possible scenario, you will hopefully learn that there are key things for you to do at certain times that will improve your care.

In order to get the best treatment when you fall ill, you should practise the communication skills we highlight at every opportunity in life so that when you really need them, you are skilled, aware, and can respond and act in a timely and appropriate manner. It is fun and enjoyable to find that you can learn skills that enhance your everyday interactions, knowing that one day, if something more serious might happen, you will be better prepared to deal with it. Lots of practise will make you a more skilled communicator so remember…

Practise, Practise, Practise.

Practise often with family and friends and you will improve.

One of the best ways of making the learning from this book stick, and become more habitually beneficial, is to 'journal' your experiences. If you really want to become great at being in control of your body and your own care, keep a written record of your conversations and interactions. Note where you had 'light bulb' moments, where you succeeded in avoiding potential errors and where, on reflection, you could have asked a better question or not just accepted what you heard. If you have ever kept a diary you will know that our recollection of the past is often very different to what actually happened or how we felt in the moment. Keeping a written record will help you reflect and prepare for your next health-related interaction.

Re-read the skills and journey sections regularly to keep your knowledge and awareness levels high.

Getting the best care comes from being more *aware* of what is happening to you, being able to ask the right questions at the right time and listening to the answers. These skills can both improve your own health outcome greatly and also help health professionals understand and do their jobs more effectively. Everybody benefits when communication and desired outcomes are clear and aligned with expectations.

We use the phrase *'healthcare professional'* throughout the book and occasionally other more specific roles where appropriate to the context. These professionals are not just doctors and nurses but also include; therapists, pharmacists, radiographers, physiotherapists – to name a few. All the behaviours and skills mentioned in this book are relevant to anyone you meet whose job it is to look after you.

Whilst we have co-authored this book, at times we share our first-hand experiences of various situations. To highlight this, we place our initials before the relevant quotes – either *RR or SJ.*

At the back of the book are two quick reference guides that briefly summarise the skills and journey sections. Use these if you need a quick refresh before you meet a healthcare professional.

CHAPTER 2

Current Reality

The NHS is an amazing thing. If you have travelled around the world, there are few places you would rather be than the UK if you need medical help. With the modern facilities, often excellent Accident and Emergency services and pioneering procedures, it is something to be proud of and a privilege to have 'free' access to. (It is of course not free; it costs billions of pounds, money most of us contribute to in taxes.)

The NHS was born out of an excellent, humanitarian ideal that 'good healthcare should be available to all, regardless of wealth' – and remains so to this day.

It is also a beast of an organisation that has approximately 1.5 million people in direct employment, with a budget of around £109 billion for 2012/13. It treats 1 million people every 36 hours – that is an extraordinary statistic!

It is little wonder that with numbers on those scales, things go wrong. It is how those errors are prevented, managed and dealt with that needs serious attention. Some work has begun to improve matters, but progress remains restricted when it's in the hands of the very people who are responsible for creating the issues in the first place.

It is likely that the majority of health professionals go to work every day and are absolutely committed to doing everything they can to help every patient they encounter get the best possible care, delivered in the most compassionate way. To these individuals we are indebted and for whom the negative publicity surrounding the NHS is a personal travesty. Were it not for these people, we would be reading a lot more negative news stories. We should all be very grateful that they have kept patient care as a primary focus despite all the distractions.

There are individuals, however, who should not be working in the NHS today and who should not be seeing you or your family. It is a fact that these individuals are in every level of the organisation, from porter to politician.

You cannot just blame 'the system'. Everything that happens is the result of an individual doing (or not doing!) something. Nothing 'just happens'. Sometimes the error made by an individual is the result of a process or system in which being the last person in the chain leaves that individual prone or likely to make an error. We can learn from other industries which have robust and well developed prevention and review systems and policies; these include aviation, oil/gas and construction. In healthcare, the prevention and review of error is in its infancy. Too many individuals shout down those raising concerns rather than learn from them – even when the concerns are causing the deaths of patients.

The reality is that the NHS has had its reputation increasingly damaged through years of political manoeuvring trying to woo voters with promises of shorter waiting lists and better services, all the while living with a structure lacking in **real accountability and responsibility**. System upon system has been introduced to try to make the figures look better, at the expense of good patient care. If the NHS was a private business it would have gone into administration years ago, but not before the dangerous and incompetent staff were fired.

An often suggested solution is to throw a few more billion pounds at the NHS as *'that will sort everything out'*. Unfortunately it won't, it's like prescribing paracetamol for a brain tumour – it may give pain relief for a while but not actually deal with the root problem.

As we write, there is a surge of 'action' to try to address the failings highlighted in the media since 2012. One of them was to instil a *'Duty of Candour'* for all NHS staff. It is a measure of the current culture that NHS employees have to be encouraged to tell the truth! Even more worrying is to then to be told that they will be offered legal protection if they dare tell the truth! The Duty of Candour campaign has good intentions behind it; to act with *honesty* and *transparency* at all times. However, it's a phrase out of touch with much of the population. A more easily understood, plain and simple phrase would have been better – TELL THE TRUTH.

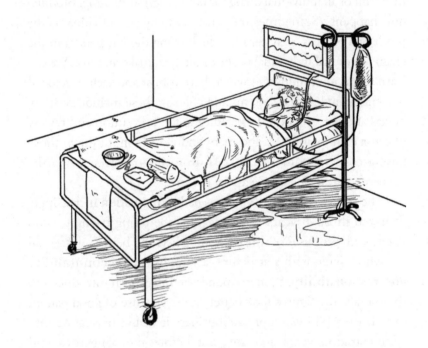

Figure 1
Is this how you see your relatives' or your own future?
What can you do to stop this happening?

Consider this thought below – if you would like to know the truth…

A lot of people don't seem to want to know, or would rather not know, or would rather *you* didn't know what they know, and don't want you to know, because then they would have

6

to actually do something – and be accountable and responsible for doing some good, which is a weird conclusion!

People would rather risk others by doing nothing rather than doing something that might help others, but by doing so leave themselves even more accountable for their evasive decision or action when the truth finally comes out later – and it will!

Now the really scary bit – despite the errors and mistakes, many major lessons are not learnt or shared nationally (in a so-called National Health Service). Some things are shared nationally, but not the errors, reasons for errors, and most certainly not the harmful impact of the cover-up of errors that has gone on for years.

Only now in 2015 is this being actively talked about, but real change is in its infancy. Too many patients who report their concerns aren't taken seriously at first.

YOU, WE, I – everyone using or who will one day need to use the NHS, all need to know how to find a way past this culture of error and cover-up to help make sure we are not harmed when it is our turn to go into hospital.

NHS staff know that error and harm happens. In some hospitals, up to 50% of staff would not be treated in their own hospital such is their own awareness of the sub-standard care on offer and more alarmingly, the failure and perceived inability to change things for the better.

This is frighteningly depressing and immensely worrying.

And it gets worse – most readers of newspapers or certain journals will know that people who try to tell the truth get ridiculed, sacked, harassed and side-lined. This has gone on for years. Step out of the herd, and so endanger the herd, and you are in for a tough time!

These people are labelled 'whistle-blowers'. Just how messed up can an organisation be when there has to be a law to allow you to tell the truth and be listened to, without fear of personal harm, harassment, being threatened with legal proceedings and losing your job?

This brings us to the next even more depressing reality: people still get side-lined and punished *despite* the legal protection. Conversations with several national groups who represent whistle-blowers have advised that given their own personal experiences, it is best, unless you are happy to risk personal ruin, to stay silent and let the culture of avoidance and denial continue. An extraordinary situation!

'Whistle-blower' however is the wrong phrase to describe people seeking fairness and justice for patients and their families. Whilst you may blow a whistle to stop something happening, it is often perceived as a piercing and uncomfortable noise that must be silenced as quickly as possible. The reason people in authority use the phrase 'whistle-blower' is that it is a noise (i.e. the truth) that they don't want to hear. The phrase is not regarded as a positive one, it has undue negative connotations synonymous with 'trouble maker'.

A much more apt label for these people is: TRUTH TELLER.

'Truth Tellers' are people who have a conscience, who have had enough of putting up with witnessing error, harm, incompetence and cover ups. They want the truth to be shared with the public so patients get the care they deserve.

Often the first thing that happens to a truth teller is a series of counter accusations to undermine them, to damage their reputation and to hope they go away quietly or withdraw their concerns. They are often accused of historical bullying, fraud, racism, or lying. All very serious accusations – strange how they only come to light once they have voiced their major concerns!

Many truth tellers were offered payments to go away quietly, having signed agreements to stay silent. Surely the people who implemented such actions should be legally held to account?

It is worth considering here just how many groups, organisations, protective bodies, regulatory bodies, parliamentary reviews, white papers, health reforms, patient support services, charities and Royal colleges have input, knowledge, influence, power and insight into NHS care. Yet despite thirty years of all their inputs, the scandals and cover-ups go on, from the sickening Savile case to the unforgivable events at Mid Staffs, Morecombe Bay, North Lincolnshire, Alder Hay, etc. They happened under everyone's noses, often with people in the profession being in the know and despite all of the above interest groups being in existence. Yet nothing was done at the *time* of the harm, and those accountable are almost all free of consequence.

It is amazing once a scandal is uncovered, how it transpires that many people either suspected or knew something was going on that should not have been. You could call this the '*Savile Syndrome*' – lots of people knew, but nobody did anything to stop it. This seems to be the case in all scandals, not just in healthcare.

Many NHS staff are embarrassed by the units they work in. You can help them regain control and pride by using the skills highlighted in this book.

Let us together stop the years of cover-ups, deceit and burial of bad news. Instead, let us have a culture of:

Admitting error,
Learning from it,
Sharing learning
and
Preventing mistakes!

What culture do we need for the NHS?

Every person employed or connected with the NHS should ask these two questions of themselves before every action and decision:

Is this what I would want for myself or my family?
Is this what the public expects me to be doing?

As the UK heads to each general election, politicians once again tell us that the NHS is only safe in their hands, conveniently forgetting or dismissing the fact that it was their previous leadership that was in place at the time of the shocking truths we have seen. Repeatedly doing the same things, making the same promises and expecting a different outcome each time is madness defined.

Culture change generally takes a long time to happen at the best of times. Waiting for real change at a political level is an even longer wait. Rather than waiting for it happen, you can be part of implementing that culture change by demanding more truth, honesty and transparency from the people who treat you, and by being better at communicating with them.

Figure 2
Transparency is about delivering honest, high quality care; not just talking about transparency!

HUMAN FACTORS

Human Factors Overview

What are Human Factors?

'Human Factors' is one of the many ways of describing the influence a person's behaviour and the culture they work in have over a given situation.

These factors include those at an:

Individual level; skills, attitudes, personality, strengths and limitations

Environmental level; culture, teamwork, leadership, workload, and communication framework

The airline industry has spent over 40 years looking at leadership, teams and behaviours, and how they relate to process and management input. The industry has specifically looked at human response to stress and challenge. They have learnt through careful, prolonged and often painful or deadly experiences that bad outcomes occur when behaviours are unchecked or are not understood, or when teams are simply unaware that natural human fallibility can lead to disaster.

This human factor training in the airline industry is now routine having become part of the basic training (1991 for Europe). Flying in commercial airliners is often regarded as the safest way to travel. Such improvement in safety needs to happen in healthcare, and is thankfully finally beginning to gain acceptance as a concept.

The key difference between a healthcare worker and a pilot is that the pilot shares the physical consequences of his error with his passengers and is therefore more motivated to do his absolute best. Apathy, laziness, disengagement and arrogance on behalf of a pilot are likely to be fatal for him as well as his passengers. A healthcare worker with the same traits goes home every day, no matter what happens to their patients.

Perhaps if all healthcare workers suffered the same fate as their patients after error and harm, standards of care would increase dramatically!

CHAPTER 3

Errors and Behaviours

No sane person goes to their place of work to intentionally make errors or cause harm.

No sane person should chose to ignore or cover up either error or harm.

Reported facts:

* Up to 20% of patients experience error or harm during the course of their treatment.[1]
* Up to 8 patients a day die because of NHS failures in safety.[2]
* There are up to 1000 preventable deaths each month in the NHS.[3]
* The NHS spends up to £1.3 <u>billion</u> a year on litigation claims![4]

These facts raise many questions: how many unsafe people work in healthcare? Are so many people really that careless, deluded, distracted, dangerous, arrogant, ignorant or psychopathic, or is it just that too many are apathetic, forgetful, lazy and self-serving? Could it be that the processes and checks in the NHS are poorly designed, implemented or followed? Could it be the focus is not on care, but on meeting political targets?

In February 2015 Health Secretary Jeremy Hunt announced an annual review into 'avoidable deaths' in hospitals – which he described as the 'biggest scandal in global healthcare'.

There is no doubt some of the systems and targets are

unhelpful and do partly explain this high rate of error. In analysis of these systems and targets the one factor that is often found at the top of the list is the attitudes and behaviours of individuals and teams, and fundamentally how they communicate. Such interaction has been studied for many years and is described by many as the culture and the 'human factors'. The airline industry has led research, developing understanding and implementing change based on the knowledge of human factors for decades. If there was a one in seven chance of injury or death from flying, most of us would be extremely reluctant to get on an aircraft! In the early years of flying, the risk of accidents or error was relatively high for those on board with sometimes tragic consequences, the effects felt by hundreds of people and their families. The same undesirable consequences of harm and error in medicine became all too clear following the Francis report.

Once upon a time, medicine was more about making a diagnosis and not much else. Little was possible with poor a understanding of disease, limited treatments or surgical ability. In the modern world, it is possible to deliver complex healthcare with many drugs, investigations and procedures. This complexity, as in aviation, increases the possibility of error and makes it increasingly possible to overload the healthcare professional. When overloaded mentally and emotionally, pilots and healthcare workers make errors. In the airline industry, genuine reassessment of skills and limited hours are mandatory and adhered to (as far as the authors know). In medicine, there is poor or no genuine reassessment, a reluctance to deal with problems, excessive hours, distraction by needless bureaucracy and mismanagement. Little wonder the error rate is so relatively high and harm occurs when poor behaviours and risk-prone systems aren't dealt with.

The healthcare service has finally begun to acknowledge that delivering good care is about more than simply spending lots of government money, making bold political statements, setting targets and making promises.

The response to many of the political initiatives in the last twenty years has been the introduction of yet more managers, implementing yet more policy documents and yet more processes and checking. Yet error and harm go on happening, only now beginning to be revealed. (It is much harder to avoid publicity when an airliner crashes or goes missing.)

As a result of political targets and demands, huge volumes of paperwork and policy review meetings take place which give the impression that real work is going on and improvements are being driven forward. 'Revalidation' is a huge bureaucracy which claims much, but is unlikely to significantly deliver safety improvements in many professionals' opinion.

The damning truth is that most of this paperwork, policy and management time has little or no effect on the improvement or the delivery of care.

The motivation and desire to do the best you can DESPITE the system comes from within individuals, and such people get little coverage or reward. Worse still, they are marginalised if they speak out and labelled 'whistle-blowers' when in fact all they aim to do is share the truth to help deliver quality patient care.

Real improvement comes from the leadership, teamwork and effort of the clinical teams delivering care and excellence, in GP surgeries, at the bed side, on a ward round, in operating theatres and those unrecognised behind the scenes in technical laboratories. The human interface is the receptionists, clerks and secretaries who provide the communication link between the frontline staff delivering care and the back-room staff analysing tests and results, thus helping you, the patient, navigate through the system.

What makes a good team work well and what makes a bad team poor? They can have the same learning, same qualifications, same professional standards and even similar time in the job, yet have vastly different outcomes for patient care. It comes down to the atmosphere or emotion within the team or, to put it another way, the accepted behaviours within the team. If they are mostly positive, reflective and supportive, harm should be avoided and error minimised. If a team generally avoids responsibility, covers up harm and does not learn from error, the effects are disastrous, with people becoming disillusioned as things go wrong, repeatedly. Worse still, this becomes normal and accepted as a usual outcome or expectation that can't and won't be changed. The *we are where we are* culture.

Ignoring the truth of what is actually going on just means things get worse.

Medicine and healthcare have at last, in the last five to ten years, begun to realise that the learning in the airline industry is equally valid in healthcare delivery. This was highlighted very clearly in an excellent BBC Horizon programme in early 2013. All healthcare professionals should be aware of these issues and learn from them.

Several hospitals in the UK now have full simulation and training facilities that can teach teams of healthcare professionals to respond to everyday healthcare issues and practise by simulating difficult problems to learn about individual and team behaviours, and how these interpersonal human factors may greatly alter the outcome for patients. The challenge right now is to get this training, learning and cultural change accepted and widely adopted. There is a resistance amongst many senior professionals to engage in or support simulated learning and assessment based on real errors and events. This is partly because they know they may be exposed as being below a satisfactory standard.

It will be a great day when every new healthcare professional has been through a pre-employment 'human factors' training programme with a long-term plan throughout their career for updating and improving performance, and every existing healthcare professional has meaningful, on-going reassessment and revalidation in both real and simulated situations. The current system of doctors choosing who to nominate for feedback to gain revalidation is deeply flawed and lacks real assessment or impartiality. Do airline pilots choose a good work 'mate' or two to re-validate their licences to continue flying passengers!?

It's all about the people

As with any organisation, there are four basic categories for NHS employees:

i.   Those who are **exceptional** – they lead, inspire, create, consider, solve problems, present solutions, openly admit mistakes, are pro-active, positive, selfless and wholly committed to the cause, and often work extra hours for which they do not either get or expect pay for. They go to work with purpose and put patients first every day. They don't take no for an answer. Ironically, they are sometimes seen as 'mavericks' and disruptive and threatening by managers and incompetent colleagues. They often leave the NHS when they have had their enthusiasm and dedication drained out of them.

ii. Those who are **good** – they work with a conscience, are competent, reliable, and trustworthy. They acknowledge mistakes and have a good level of self and social awareness. They also put patients first.

iii. Those who are **average** – they think it's just a job, they often work to rule, use systems and rules as an excuse to not get things done, do a reasonable job most of the time and occasionally give hope. They get caught up in negative, destructive dialogue and regularly engage in gossip and blame. They often put themselves first.

iv. Those who are **dangerous** – they are deluded, they think they are better than they are, they are actually incompetent, fraudulent, cause harm, lie, cover up mistakes, have a fragile ego and often unduly self-promote. They are at every level of the NHS. They very rarely face the consequences they deserve because managers are under pressure to focus on managing the figures, not managing the people.

As a patient, how are you to know from which category is the healthcare employee in front of you? The person who you hope is going to make you better!

Ask yourself, what proportions of the above people do you think make up your NHS?

A top tip – Find out who is trustworthy and competent in a healthcare setting by asking the staff what they see and hear, especially the healthcare assistants, ward clerks and cleaners. These essential staff are at the bottom of the pay scale usually working hard delivering day to day care and compassion. They have no hierarchal elevation and are the eyes and ears of the health setting, quietly noticing and listening, as everyone tells them everything there being no perceived status barrier or fear of consequence. They know everything, see everything and hear everything. Befriend them and listen to them. Ask them, if they needed treatment, who would they choose to care for them?

Learning from error

Some of the following culture is growing in the NHS. However the processes are incomplete and don't always fully result in meaningful actions. Of the list below, only 1 and 2 probably happen everywhere, 3 should, but for points 4-7 it is not clear from the practices of 2013 that they are followed.

1. Report all errors or near misses (so called IR1 systems reporting forms).
2. Investigate thoroughly events and facts leading to an error (RCA Risk Cause Analysis).

1 and 2 are in place in most, if not all health organisations.

3. Implement rapid change to prevent recurrence (new protocol, checklist or modification).

You would hope and expect 3 to naturally flow from 1 and 2. However, change is often met with stubborn resistance or worse, refusal to accept the need to change or learn. Errors are 'explained away' by spurious means or by ignoring compounding factors, often behavioural, as too difficult to deal with. Even agreed positive change can take months, and sometimes years to come about. Often a series of meetings results in a phenomenon known as 'regression to the mean', when dilution means good intentions are diluted until nothing changes. So the steps below are what should happen next:

4. Look ahead at possible likely errors and put in preventative steps.
5. Everyone in the team shares safety responsibility and is free to act.
6. Share widely the lessons in an unbiased, national professional forum.
7. Open sharing of knowledge within teams and with the public.

The CQC (Care Quality Commission), set up to look at healthcare and hospital safety, has itself been under investigation having been accused of deleting a report which exposed their own failures to act on concerns about a Trust. (Morecambe Bay Hospitals 2010[5]) Making the CQC job impossible was being sandwiched between hospitals changing 'never events' and 'Death Rate Criteria', and politicians only wanting to publicise good news stories. As of 2014, a more vigorous CQC and inspection team evolved with 'champions' to carry out thorough, detailed and unannounced inspections.

These new CQC inspections will look at the broader range of cultural and behavioural aspects of operations along with standard data measures. These inspection teams we hope will reveal any serious cultural issues and enforce positive changes that are in the interests of the patients. To achieve this, these new inspection teams will have to have leadership that is humble, honest and brave enough to reveal and deal with the uncomfortable truths that do exist. Only by doing this will there be any real progress to drag the

NHS out of its all too comfortable culture of apathy to a place that is consistently safe and acts with integrity.

> For good things to happen, some uncomfortable truths have to be revealed and dealt with first.
>
> Simply acknowledging and moving on is not enough.

This book will help you to learn more about these human-influenced issues. In the age of information there is very little to stop anyone with the desire to learn finding out about their own 'human factors' and behaviours. You can then be in a better place to understand how you interact with the health system, and develop a greater awareness of your own and others' needs. With dedication you can remain more in control of your needs and avoid, or at least minimise the fallibility and error-prone behaviour that we are all at risk of. We can learn to help each other address these fallibilities to get the best care for you, your family and ultimately everyone else.

Information is no longer the secret power of the educated
or the professionals.
Most knowledge is only 1 or 2 clicks away
It is all about how we use knowledge TOGETHER,
for GOOD.

CHAPTER 4

Responsibility & Accountability

Two words which you will see many times in this book and hear numerous people use in the media – *responsibility* and *accountability*. But what do they actually mean and how does the use of them (or not) influence your care?

They are important words that are key to the level of care you receive. You should understand what they mean and who has these labels when it comes to you being treated. Responsibility is especially the one that you will hear politicians use frequently, *"We need people to take responsibility."* However, have you ever heard a senior politician or hospital CEO publicly disclose what they are accountable and responsible for, BEFORE a crisis occurs? Every public servant's job description should have these two words in it and a list of clear answers to define them, open to anyone who wishes to read them.

These words are far too easy to just throw around as important soundbites just because they sound serious or add gravitas to a conversation or speech. To give them real meaning, there are two supplementary questions to ask:

Who is **responsible** and for what?

Who is **accountable**, for what and to whom?

Any conscientious, ethical leader who is driven by values will have these two questions answered and clearly communicated at all levels of the organisation.

Responsibility

By definition is: **something within one's power, control or management.**

Your GP is responsible for prescribing you the correct drugs, your surgeon is responsible for performing the correct procedure, and your nurse is responsible for monitoring and recording your vital signs in hospital. YOU are responsible for following your physiotherapy plan, for taking your pills according to the guidelines and for following specific advice on diet and exercise. In other words, there is a shared responsibility for your care at many levels – and you are included!

One of the main issues is that managers are mostly responsible for hitting targets, not for ensuring healthcare teams deliver excellent patient care. When you follow the food chain to the top, you will see why. Politicians want to be responsible for improved figures so they can look like they care.

Blame cultures exist when there are no clear guidelines or definitions on who is responsible and for what. When people say, "Oh that's not my job," or, "They have 'Teflon shoulders'," it's a sure sign there is no culture of people taking responsibility.

Sigmund Freud poses this thought...

"Most people do not really want freedom, because freedom involves responsibility, and most people are frightened of responsibility."

It takes certain qualities to want responsibility; character, duty, care, integrity, hard work...

It's clear that at Mid-Staffs there were serious gaps in responsible behaviour.

Doug Larson offers this quote which sums up the negative blame that politicians dish out on each other on a daily basis...

"The reason people blame things on the previous generation is that there's only one other choice." (Taking responsibility)

As patients, we expect that all healthcare staff will take responsibility in the moment to do the right thing for us.

Accountability

'To be held to account'. i.e. the people whose job it is to enforce standards.

Who is the person or persons that are either going to take the glory or the shame for what happens at the sharp end or point of delivery? In business, if the company makes a big profit, the board take the glory as they are accountable to the shareholders. In the BP Deepwater Horizon oil spill in the Gulf of Mexico, it was reported that the CEO left the company as he was ultimately accountable for the actions of his staff and the systems in place. It was his job to enforce standards as the leader of the business.[6] He still got a severance package which slightly defeats the point of being held accountable! The captain of a ship can be prosecuted if a ship runs aground even if he was in bed at the time when one of his officers was on watch and in command. The officer was responsible, but the Captain is ultimately accountable.

Of all the NHS scandals that have been exposed over the last few years, how many people have actually been held to account for what went so wrong? How many of those senior managers are still employed in the NHS? Which politician or health minister has accepted that they were accountable and resigned?

If you know you will not personally suffer as a result of serious incidents, then why would you take more personal responsibility for what is actually going on? Think major NHS failures, banking crisis, child protection scandals, libor rate…

Accountability should be clear and defined for all organisations, teams and individuals with the consequences of failing to meet the expectations made clear. If more (senior) people were genuinely held to account, levels of individual responsibility **and** accountability would trickle down the organisational structure. If this happened in the NHS – you the 'patient' would benefit and less errors should happen because people would be thinking more about exactly what they are supposed to be doing.

If you find yourself in hospital, perhaps you could ask the staff those two questions already mentioned:

Who is **responsible** for my care for what will they be doing?

Who is **accountable** for the quality of my care? Do *they* know?

Clear Accountability breeds more Responsibility.

Figure 3
Who is accountable and for what?

Phrases you may hear staff saying which are good examples
of individuals avoiding responsibility and placing blame on
'the system':

"We are where we are."

"Let's wait and see what happens."

"Let's not do anything now as things will only change in
the future."

CHAPTER 5

Personal Agendas

In an organisation as big as the NHS, with such a huge number of people working in it, it should come as no surprise that personal agendas are prevalent, and part of the everyday dynamics that directly affect the level of care you receive as a patient.

Agendas exist for a number of reasons and probably originate from early in the development of humans under the banner of self-preservation. *"I just need to do what is best for me, so I survive."* Agendas are a complex subject as they are linked to individuals' values, beliefs and needs. They are the things that are deep within each and every one of us, they drive us and inform us on the decisions we make and the actions we follow.

People join organisations but leave because of their managers. This is usually down to a mis-match of agendas (and values). Agendas can have a positive or negative outcome on relationships. The behaviours used to fulfill an agenda can be inclusive and productive or selfish and destructive. The key question for anyone to ask themselves when they do something is:

"What is my REAL intention?"

i.e. – *'what are the actual reasons I did that or suggested that?'*. When you post a comment or picture of you on a lovely beach on facebook, what are the **real** reasons for doing so? *Bringing joy to others? Recognition? To instigate envy? Hey look at me, bet you wish you were here?*

If all healthcare staff had an increased conscious level of awareness as to their real intentions, and remained focused on the primary agenda (YOU!) you would get better care. The simulation training we have run and mention in the book is a great way of revealing a person's hidden agendas that they may not be aware of.

A doctor who wants to make changes to a clinical service to improve efficiency to see more patients has a positive agenda. The intent being about putting patients first.

A manager who ignores other people's ideas, so they can make their own idea happen, has a negative agenda. His 'intent' is a need for recognition, status, job security, and is self-serving.

The best care happens when all staff have the same agenda:

> 'The provision of high-quality care that is safe, effective and focused on patient experience.'[7]
> (One of the NHS's guiding principles)

What are the harmful effects on others because of entrenched personal agendas?

Some personal agendas can have catastrophic consequences for patients. If staff are more interested in their own position, authority, professional status, positional power, or other personal needs, than they are in the care they deliver, it is obvious that the patient will not get the level of care they expect. Think of all the national scandals that have happened and the ones that we have mentioned – what personal agendas were present that ended up being so destructive and harmful? When there is a lack of openness about agendas, it can lead to deceit, mistrust and poor performance.

> *RR – In the 24 years I've worked in the NHS, there is not a single hospital where I have not regularly heard medical staff (including consultants) refer to managers as liars, and heard many managers refer to doctors as being useless. With such an ingrained lack of trust and cohesion, is it any wonder that patient care has suffered?*

If a surgeon repeatedly cancels his patients from his operating lists, what could his agenda be?

There are very few people who can work and live without personal agendas. Every time we contribute to a conversation, express an opinion or make a decision, there is often a reason (agenda) behind it. If you have a conversation with friends about what pub to go to, your reasons will be linked to your agenda; is it closer to your home? Is it cheaper so you can spend less? Is it because you have some other friends going to that pub who you would also like (or rather!) see? We are rarely unconditionally open about our agendas!

Practise explaining your rationale for a decision or action next time you find yourself expressing an opinion – it won't be very far away!

Better care can be given to patients by staff who practise the values of humility, service, and integrity. Putting others first and self last should be the daily priority. Sometimes we have to put ourselves first when we are ill for example – but really staff should not be in work if they can't put the patient first.

WHAT IS BEST FOR THE PATIENT?

When staff are surrounded by the conflicting priorities of rapidly changing agendas set by politicians and managers, it can be extremely difficult to keep the patient as their first priority. NHS Managers spend more time managing the figures than their staff – because it fits their own agenda.

We will talk about types of questions in the communication skills chapter. If you want to know the agenda behind someone's intent, ask them WHY? questions. These can be very challenging conversations though as it will expose their inner needs, belief and core values.

There are some fundamental rules on agendas that we should be aware of, as below:

1. Everyone has their own agenda (understandably).
2. Only occasionally do people share the same agenda and if they do, rarely at the same time.
3. The primary agenda for every NHS employee and politician should be to provide the best possible quality treatment with patients fully engaged in their own care.
4. Conflicting agendas don't help the patient.

'Managers value what can be measured, as opposed to measuring what is valued.'

Figure 4
Negative personal agendas don't help you, the patient

The press has repeatedly raised our awareness of the phrase 'reputational management', which summarises the manager's agenda of securing their individual position, regardless of what is going on around them. This attitude of **'me first'**, is short-sighted,

31

likely to harm patients and will eventually harm the misguided individual themselves.

A common response to the unmasking of harm and cover-up since the Francis report has been to put posters around hospitals stating how care, compassion, teamwork and safety are the hospital's top priority. Surely these have always been the patient's expectations!? Putting up a poster is marketing over substance.

There are, however, some recent examples where senior leaders are engaging on the clinical front at the bedside and alongside the staff who deliver care. Examples from Holland suggest patients are being regularly invited to help run hospitals, attending key decision meetings about the services they use. This is positive and should be more widespread and adopted quickly if proven to be successful.

Very few major crises just **happen** overnight; they may **appear** overnight, but a lack of clear leadership over a prolonged period of time combined with conflicting agendas leads to catastrophic situations where many patients suffer.

(Time^2 + Lack of leadership) x Conflicting agendas = Disaster

CHAPTER 6

Power and Ego

Figure 5
Is this your doctor?

Becoming a politician, chief executive, senior doctor or nurse brings title and perceived power. How is this used?

We, the public, hope and expect people with position or title to use their status to better the health service. We really appreciate talented people being down to earth, approachable, human, honest, communicative, warm and caring.

Most people in the health profession start off with this in mind, but some don't and yet more become disenchanted by working in the health service and adopt poor survival or coping strategies. Just about any attitude is tolerated, which, despite being unacceptable, is allowed because of the general perception that a health professional with status must ultimately have our best interests at heart, have trained for a long time and so must be worth keeping. Poor performers are often slowly retired and sometimes even promoted to get them out of the way!

There is a malignant culture of avoidance of responsibility and accountability when things go wrong, when concerns are raised and worse still a completely unacceptable culture of cover up and denial. The Francis report made hundreds of recommendations; but who is implementing them? – The very management structure that has accepted the poor culture that led to the report! How can all this be happening?

Given we trust that no one is crazy enough to set out to work each day thinking, 'What can I bury, avoid and lie about today?' (at least they would not write that on their job application), then why do so many people in senior positions adopt such destructive behaviours?

One reason is self-preservation and a need to survive at all costs. This is separate to having a competitive nature. Competitive sport teaches the importance of winning humbly and losing gracefully, seeking to improve for the next challenge. The attitude of senior status-driven individuals is, 'I am never wrong, never lose, and never admit'; this is clearly dangerous. This attitude is a mixture of conflicting insecurities in a setting of perceived status and expectation leading to dangerous arrogance. This has been written about in the book '*Naked Pilot*' by David Beaty[8] – an excellent read for all professionals and lay people who want to understand how hierarchy and title combined with, ego, herd and survival instincts affect people when stressed by demanding situations.

RR – Some examples of this in my career:

"How dare you question my authority and expertise?"
"No, I don't need your help; I know what I am doing."
"Shut up." and *"Shut the f@*k up."*
"I am bigger than you."
"I am your senior colleague. Do as you are told, or you will never work again."

Similar attitudes between senior pilots and junior co-pilots in years gone by led to catastrophic errors when the senior would not listen to a junior pointing out an obvious error.

These attitudes can still be seen in medicine amongst senior and even new staff who mimic what has gone before them. Egotistical seniors and some juniors refuse to listen, dismiss alternative ideas and get angry if challenged by people they see as junior or inferior. A favourite threat is the, *'Cross me and you'll never work again'* or the shot across the bows of, *'I do believe there were concerns raised about you some time ago'* or a deliberate campaign to maximise disciplinary process over a minor matter. One particularly obnoxious senior refers to junior colleagues even over forty years old as 'kids'. (And also to old disabled people as, "Them f***in old people in wheelchairs.")

Of course it's not just those at the frontline who fight their personal ego duels, often giving the patient the lowest priority. The culture in any organisation comes from the top and ultimately for the NHS it is set by the politicians whose deceit, expense fraud, half-truths, acceptance of bribes, denial of responsibility for error, audacity in joking about disasters (there is no money left) with an arrogant 'it's no longer my problem, mate' attitude, whilst at the same time often claiming the moral high ground on any given issue. It is little surprise that the NHS cultural integrity as a whole is at a very low level, when hypocrisy and deviant behaviour is thought smart and acceptable by those who lead. Many politicians (and others in authority) have a somewhat ironic and sanctimonious approach of apologising, being humble and shocked – but only after being found out!

It would appear that for too many people, power and ego breeds contempt and arrogance.

> Many, many professionals do a great job, work extremely hard, deliver great care with compassion and do all this despite the power games, egos and political interference.

A favourite story is of a junior doctor answering a ward phone to be shouted at by the senior doctor, a professor. When the junior was unable to help the irate professor in a timely manner, the professor shouted, "Do you know who I am?" "Yes," replied the junior adding, "Do you know who I am?" The even more irate professor said, "No!" to which the cheeky junior replied, "Well, f*@k off then!"

Given the long-running toxic levels of interpersonal competition and ego clashes, it is little wonder error and harm occur. Individuals take joy in others' mishaps and mistakes and relish the chance to air these little victories at management meetings, rather than put positive teamwork and patient care first. We wonder whether the priming of young people with the sentiment that doctors and nurses are so special and extremely important – and in the case of doctors the cream of the school and college – trains individuals' brains into an arrogant, elitist mind-set that stays with them for life. Cultural stereotypes that differ, seen in overseas trained doctors, can also manifest as obstacles to communication and effectiveness. For example, some cultures see females as inferior. This is a huge issue given the high proportion of females working in the NHS.

We need professionals to let go of their egos, we need people with 'power' to listen and be wise, demonstrating long-term, clear thinking based on others' needs, not just their own immediate goals and rewards. When told by a patient, "Well, you are the 'expert'" (i.e. you are fully responsible for me), the response should be, *"I am very knowledgeable but not infallible"*. In others words, 'I am here to help the best I can, and we share responsibility equally'.

As a patient, how can power and egos influence your care?

Having an ego in itself is no bad thing – if it matches personal ability and the perceptions of others. Ego becomes a problem when it is elevated by self to a level that is not matched by ability. Whilst seeing a healthcare professional with a large ego may be unpleasant as an experience, if they deliver great care then it is bearable. The issue for these people is that professional arrogance can come across as unpleasant to some patients.

The following combinations are worth considering. It is for you as a patient to decide which you would prefer to be treated by!

1. Arrogance + Ability = Good Outcome
2. Arrogance + Ignorance = Poor Outcome
3. Affable + Ability = Good Outcome
4. Affable + Ignorance = Poor Outcome

Clearly you want combination 1 or 3 – but how do you find out the levels of someone's ability?

1. As we mention in the 'Being in Hospital' chapter, ask the staff (clerks/cleaners/nurses) who gets good results.
2. Ask your healthcare worker direct questions about outcomes and gauge their responses.
3. Check national performance and audit data as it becomes available.

If you are unlucky enough to be sat in front of a healthcare professional who you struggle to communicate with and makes you feel uncomfortable, ask to see someone else.

COMMUNICATION
SKILLS

Communication Skills and Decision Making Overview

Communication – quite possibly the most overused 'buzz word' in recent history. Perform a Google search and you get over 250,000,000 pages to read from. Search Amazon books and choose from over 600,000 titles. So with all that information out there, surely we are all great at communicating?

It seems baffling then that with every error and every enquiry, both in healthcare and elsewhere, poor communication comes out high on the list of reasons of what went wrong, and is the topic that needs to be much improved in the future. A future that oddly keeps repeating itself like some terrible movie plot!

So what on earth, in the name of our sanity and safety, is going on?

When you are a team of one, you have 100% of the accountability and are responsible for everything that happens to you. If you are a fox trapper living in a remote part of the Arctic, life is actually quite simple because you don't have to speak to anyone!

As soon as you have to interact and converse with another human, we enter a convoluted world of judgement, interpretation, facts, attitudes, beliefs, understanding, opinions, agendas, intelligence, selfishness, education, ego, power, assumption, control, desires, attitudes, needs and focus, to name but a few reasons. Stir into this mix some hormonal emotion (male or female) and feelings and it's little wonder conversations and the subsequent outcomes don't always go as well as they could have done. We are complex creatures when it comes to communication.

With poor communication there is often a lack of clarity around who is making the decisions, who is accountable, who is responsible, and what the plan is. This is when error happens and in the case of patient care, you are the person who can suffer. Blame cultures are common within NHS departments – and just about every other organisation. They happen when there is a lack of clarity, trust, understanding, honesty, accountability and the ability to ask the right questions to check understanding. There are numerous references to the aviation industry in this book as there is much to learn and transpose into healthcare. Checking the understanding of the situation by aircrew is paramount in the safe operation of an aircraft. As a patient, we expect healthcare staff to communicate to a high level and do all the necessary checks and balances that are in our best interests. But what can you do as a patient to make sure that the chances of error or harm to you are minimised?

Unlike aviation, where you don't really have the opportunity to question the people whose hands you are putting your life in, there are many opportunities in healthcare for you to take some responsibility to question staff and check understanding. Many 'never events' would have been prevented had the patient or staff colleague asked the most simple of questions.

The pilot of an aircraft would get quite annoyed if every passenger asked him questions like, "Can I check we are going to the same destination?"; "Do we have enough fuel to get there?"; "What is your understanding of our flight path today?"; "How many times have you landed this type of aircraft?" and, "What's your error record?"

But you can and should ask your surgeon/doctor/nurse similar yet simple crucial questions.

Some of you reading this will be asking, "Why should I have to check understanding and ask questions of healthcare staff; isn't it their job to get it right?" Well yes, it is their job, but mistakes happen and simply because you can, you should, and because in doing so, you could save your life.

Unconditional trust is often given because you assume and accept that because someone has all the qualifications, a lofty job title or, in the case of doctors, historical social admiration, that they will be competent. However if do that, you may find that it's pretty much tantamount to personal negligence on your own behalf. Some trust is invariably given, but full trust is only truly developed through having a quality conversation to establish a mutual understanding that is followed by a performance aligned to your expectations. In simple terms, trust is the firm belief in someone's ability, reliability and honesty.

Trust is maintained when outcomes match expectations

Holding a 'quality conversation' is a skill and an art that needs conscious practice in order to improve and do effectively. Being able to have a quality conversation comprising focused, constructive dialogue is a critical element in the quality of the healthcare you receive. If you walk out of a meeting with a health professional upset, confused, frightened or even angry, you know that you have not had a quality conversation! Wouldn't it be good to have some control and skills in communication to stop such events?

The two main elements of communication and a quality conversation that can have the greatest positive influence for you as the patient are your ability to ask **great questions** and your ability to **listen.** We will look at these specific skills in depth in the next two chapters and provide you with the skills, knowledge and ways of practising them. With the right knowledge you can then make the best decision for you. We will cover the main points of decision-making at the end of the communication section.

When it comes to your care, there should be a conversation that results in *you* being able to make an informed decision, based on your understanding of the facts, that's best for *you*.

A simple flow:

You ask questions
You listen
You ask more questions

You summarise your understanding
You make decisions and form a plan that's best for you

Communication – from the Latin word 'to share'.

Some healthcare professionals are proactive in developing their communication skills and some much less so. A skilled communicator will help you, using a similar structure to that above, without you even realising. Many healthcare workers think that their job is to tell patients what's best for them. We believe this is not the case. Their job is to:

Serve patients with the facts so the patient can make an informed decision, which is in the patient's own best interests.

SJ – On one occasion, I ran a communication skills workshop for some Consultant Surgeons. On setting up a simple practical exercise to the group of twenty doctors where they had the opportunity to practise questioning and listening, I noticed three of them had stood up and started to follow me around the room as I listened in to the paired discussions. On asking them to sit down and practise they replied, "Oh but we are very senior and don't need the practise." It is these people with large and fragile egos who are deluded and a danger to patients.

It's often said, *"You can't teach an old dog new tricks."* I'd say, *"An arrogant old dog can certainly damage your health."*

CHAPTER 7

An Introduction to the Power of Questions

The Power of Questions

So often in life we are unsatisfied with the information we have received, whether it be from the insurance company, the airline staff or the health professional. How often do we reflect on whether we asked the right questions to get the desired information? We often just think that they were an idiot or just didn't know! But how about some self-reflection to consider what part you played in generating the responses you heard?

In this chapter we explore the power of questions and how learning to ask the right questions will help you receive better healthcare.

If you wanted to know what time it was, what question would you ask?

How about: "Excuse me, what time is it please?" Okay – this seems obvious but people regularly overcomplicate their questions for many reasons and are then dissatisfied and confused with the response.

If you wanted to know what time it was, why on earth would you say: "So, if you were to look at a clock and observe the numbers and position of the hands, and based on clocks you have seen before and taking into account the information you have, how would you describe what you see?"

A slightly protracted example but hopefully you see the point!

Every extra unnecessary word you put in a question gives you a diminishing return on the quality of the answer you require and will receive, and runs the risk of you compromising your relationship with the person you are talking to.

Start noticing and you will see daily examples of people overcomplicating questions and receiving unhelpful answers and asking poor quality questions that have a negative impact on the relationship.

How about that chap we recently heard asking in a bar: "So what's the closest thing you have to a Pina Colada?"

The barman replied, after a short pause: "A Pina Colada."

If you examine the motivation and intent behind the question there is a level of assumption that they don't serve the drink and likely a level of judgement about the venue or barman.

The question made it difficult for the barman to say anything other the facts that made the patron feel and look visibly embarrassed, resulting in an instantly compromised relationship. But it was his own fault for not asking the simple question: "Do you serve Pina Coladas?"

People overcomplicate and ask poor quality questions for a number of reasons including not really wanting to hear the answer or the truth. Underlying reasons may be through nerves and fear; trying to appear knowledgeable on a subject; the need for control, power, ego, judgement or liking the sound of their own voice too much!

PRACTISE and NOTICE!

Engage yourself in some deliberate practice at being more aware of the questions you hear yourself and other people asking and what the responses are like in relation to the questions. How could you or someone else have asked a more simple and better quality question?

There are many opportunities for noticing on TV, radio, in films, with friends, and in everyday society.

The best questions are the questions a child would ask. Short, simple and direct. In fact, a good way of framing your questions is to ask yourself, 'How would a child ask the question to find out the information I require?'

Your questions need not be complex; the shorter the better. It makes it easier for the recipient to answer and it clarifies what you actually want to know. Short questions are more memorable and it *should be* easier for you to understand if you have got a clear and honest answer.

When you ask any question in any situation, first ask yourself, **'What do I *really* want to know?'** Now think of the *simplest* question that will give you that information..

Ask yourself...

"What do I really want to know?"

Many people will just ask the wrong question, accept the answer given, then walk away dissatisfied.

If you want to know why so many of us do this, read 'Fast and Slow Thinking' by Daniel Kahneman.[9]

Common good questions for patients to ask:

* ★ What is wrong with me?
* ★ Is this going to hurt?
* ★ How bad are the side effects?
* ★ What are the facts?
* ★ How long will I wait?
* ★ What has led you to that conclusion?
* ★ Why do you think that?
* ★ What are my options?

And the one question that nearly every patient is thinking but rarely asks:

* ★ Am I going to die?

These are all great questions; short, simple, clear.

We will now help you really understand how to use questions to get the best care possible for you and your family.

We often overcomplicate our questions because we have some knowledge, want to share our wisdom, have done some internet research or are nervous. Considering your questions is key to getting the information you require. We will cover this in the 'Your Health Journey' sections.

> "If you ask a question and don't get the information you need, you probably asked the wrong question."

May not be true if you were lied to, or were speaking to someone incompetent, devious and or who had an agenda and an interest in misleading you – and who was probably trying to avoid responsibility. Just watch the BBC's 'Question Time' programme.

If you ask a question to another person and they respond by either laughing, ignoring you or totally changing the subject, they may well have something to hide. This could be guilt, truth, inability, error or harm.

So why don't we ask questions? Well that's a good question! In the case of healthcare professionals, and specifically doctors, it is mainly because we offer too much deferential behaviour to the esteemed god-like figure behind the desk. You and they have to realise that *you* are in the position of power – it's your body! So ask questions, and good ones at that!

In all walks of life we fail to ask questions because we make assumptions and think that others should or will have already thought about it and acted accordingly. Unsure what's happening? Ask questions.

Some of us adopt 'victim status' and just wait to see what happens to us – then complain when dissatisfied. Ask questions –

earlier. It is far better to **prevent** error and harm, rather than react after it has happened.

Here is a challenge for you – can you think of a single problem in the history of mankind that has been solved without a question being asked?

Questions are key to solving problems, developing understanding, fostering relationships, challenging assumptions, reducing uncertainty... the list goes on.

If you ask a question that requires an opinion and you don't get a straight answer that you understand, then try re-asking the question using a scale format. Using scales or percentages will let you know how confident the healthcare worker is in the conviction of their opinion.

People in authority often offer long rambling answers to direct questions because they either don't know the answer or they don't have an opinion... or they don't want you to know they don't know or don't have an opinion!

The other permutation is that they do indeed have an opinion – but they don't want to share it with you because they have a personal agenda.

For example:

Q – Have I got glaucoma?

The non-direct answer – *"Well, this is a very complex disease requiring multiple investigations and repeat visits, and it's only after working out"*... etc, etc.

Q – On a scale of 0-10, have I got glaucoma? (0 being no, and 10 being yes)

If you now get an answer of 0 – you are clear you do not have glaucoma!

If you get an answer of 10 – you have glaucoma. If either a 0 or a 10, then you can ask, "What is *the clear evidence for this certainty? – Please explain."*

If you get an answer of 5 on any scale-based question, i.e. 50% – it is likely that the individual answering has no clear idea and it's just a fact-less opinion, or a guess.

Not knowing is not a crime, but not sharing the TRUTH that you don't know IS.

A friend used a percentage type question during a recent consultation. "What percentage likelihood do I have of making a full recovery?" "80%," said the surgeon. The follow up question being, "What gives you 20% of doubt?"

Opinions should be backed up with concrete facts. It is your job to ask the right questions to get the facts. Opinions are given based on a number of factors: experience, judgement, guesswork and hunches. As a patient, you need to get the FACTS!

They call it 'practising medicine' for a reason – that it is impossible to know everything due to the sheer complexity of the human body. It is little wonder then that healthcare workers use guesswork as they 'practise' their trade. Detect the guesswork and ask the right questions to get the facts.

If you ask a really good, simple and clear question, this is exactly the kind of answer you should be very suspicious of…

If you recall the TV programme '*Yes, Prime Minster*', Sir Humphrey may have answered like this…

"Based on the balance of probabilities, taking into account all current known knowns and sidestepping and ignoring the known unknowns and mitigating errors and fallibility of presumed assumptions and deflecting reasonable doubt, and taking into account the current needs of the organisation, you probably have a small risk of glaucoma and eventual blindness in the fullness of time, but at this current time I would suggest delaying any actual decision until further evidence and disclosure of knowns and unknowable knowns become clearer."

The power of a good question
1.   It makes people think
2.   It generates responsibility
3.   It provides clarity and facts
4.   It provides information
5.   It highlights assumptions
6.   It can promote a deeper understanding

It is undoubtedly a matter of fact that the better you are at questioning and listening, the better the chance of receiving top class healthcare from the people whose job it is to look after you.

It is a professional healthcare worker's privilege to look after you. By questioning them, you can reinforce that it is their duty and privilege to have your trust; is not just your privilege to be sat in front of them.

An exercise

Think about the last time you saw a health professional and consider the following questions:

* What do your remember about the conversation?
* How much were you listened to?
* How involved did you feel in making decisions?
* How much control did you have?
* How did you feel when you left the conversation?
* What questions do you wish you had asked?

Think through your answers and share with your relatives and friends having asked them to complete the same exercise.

What are the key themes? Write down the most common things that are said and experienced then think through what that means to you. If you have seen a good health professional, and we hope you have, then this will be an easy and rewarding task. If it is not so great a memory, then consider how you would or could change things next time for you to be in control and feel more informed.

Types of Questions

There are many types of questions but to keep this simple, let's concentrate on the two main types of questions: OPEN AND CLOSED.

OPEN – Use if you want **information.**

CLOSED – Use if you want **clarity**. If asked correctly, it is a YES or NO answer.

For example:

OPEN
"What do you think is wrong with me?" – You find out lots of information and possibilities.

CLOSED
"Have I got cancer?" – You discover specifics. Yes/No.

Words which you can use at the start of OPEN questions to get information and build your understanding:

WHAT?
HOW?
WHEN?
WHO?
WHERE?
WHY?

Words which you can use at the start of CLOSED questions to give you clarity:

IS?
IF?
COULD?
WOULD?
WILL?
DO?
WAS?
WILL?

A note on using the 'WHY' question:

Not always, but asking a WHY question can be challenging for the recipient. Being asked WHY can make the person feel that they should justify their position or opinion or are being judged. Sometimes this is a good thing though! If you feel you are unclear why a healthcare worker is advocating a certain point, then ask the WHY question.

WHY questions can probe deeply very quickly because they force you to answer based on your beliefs, attitudes and opinions. Other OPEN questions direct the recipient to answer with facts. WHY question answers often involve emotion-based responses.

If you have ever been stopped by the police for speeding, they may well ask, "So WHY were you doing 95mph today on the motorway?" It instantly makes you feel guilty!

WHY questions can be very useful, but their overuse or delivery in a confrontational way will almost certainly compromise your relationship – in any walk of life.

A real depth of understanding is only reached by asking what we call 'building questions'. These are questions that directly relate to what you have just heard, and build on each other. Having a pre-prepared list of questions is great, but just going through them routinely without exploring each one in depth is where much is missed. This exploration is where you need to practise deep listening, which we discuss in the next section.

If you notice interviewers on TV and radio, many just go through their list of questions without asking any building questions, often missing real gems of opportunity to investigate further. It's often visible on TV as the camera pans to the interviewer to see them reading their next question and not being engaged at all in a quality conversation.

As a patient, you need to develop the ability to ask building questions to help you get the best care. PRACTISE.

In healthcare, it is prudent for you to have control over what is going to happen to you. You can do this by asking good questions to those looking after you. Being able to influence outcomes that are in your interest is an important skill. We are all individuals but our behaviours might be neatly summarised as below. Where do you fit in?

Broadly there are three types of people:

1. Those that make things happen;
2. Those that watch what happens; and
3. Those that ask, "What the hell happened?"

The tragic irony for the people in group 3 is that this may be the first question they have ever asked and it may already be too late!

To be in control you have to lead and take responsibility which means being in the first group. You can start to make things happen by asking great questions.

How are you going to learn and acquire the skills highlighted here? Reading this book is a great start, then practise the skills as suggested and review how much difference it makes to your understanding and satisfaction. With practise, you will become more aware of:

* What questions achieve
* What different questions achieve

* Which questions to ask and when
* When to stop asking questions
* Which questions get reactions
* Which questions challenge people
* Which are good questions and which are bad ones

Remember: practise, practise, practise...
and then reflect on the outcomes of the types of questions used.

CHAPTER 8

Listening and Summarising

Figure 6
A communication exercise

Study the picture above. What do you see going on? Put yourself in the position of each character – what would you be doing or saying? Who is listening to you?

LISTENING

Learning to Listen!

Having read the section before this one, you should have become aware of how clear communicating is about good questioning, but as you will learn and experience in this chapter, listening to responses thoughtfully is crucial to the quality of your healthcare. You have learnt how to ask good questions – your next challenge is to learn how to listen – and practise it.

So you think you are a good listener? Are you sure about that?

When asked the question about the characteristics of good communication, many of us think that it's about being articulate, knowledgeable, and *talking*. Rarely does anyone ever *initially* say that it's about LISTENING. One of the best quotes has to be:

> *"You have two ears and one mouth, use them in appropriate proportions."*

Having an ability to really focus on what is being said, to process it, consider it, and think about what questions to ask is a real skill that only comes with deliberate practice.

So why don't we listen very well? Well, we are pretty much hardwired to judge everything we hear, and say what we think about it – either internally or out loud, and to do it quickly. No matter what you hear, it is very hard to suspend personal judgement in the moment and just *absorb* and *accept* what you are hearing.

If a friend told you they had a headache, what's the first thing you would do?

1. Think if you also have a headache
2. Tell them you also have a headache
3. Ignore the comment and talk about something else entirely

4. Acknowledge their state and ask a few light questions; or
5. Ask them some questions about their headache to get a deep understanding.

If you are at 4 or 5 you have displayed some genuine listening ability!

TASK: Tell your family and friends you have a headache and see what happens!

Listening can be labelled in a number of ways depending on the level of engagement with you:

Disengaged – Not taking any notice whatsoever of what was said and recalling nothing from the conversation.

Polite – Someone may nod and acknowledge, but they are likely to be thinking about something else entirely. They are probably wishing they had never engaged you in conversation and are thinking of how to end the conversation and move on as soon as possible.

Passive – They are having a conversation with you and taking some interest but are likely judging you and talking about themselves. They may interrupt, and can't wait for you to breathe so they have some space to start talking!

Active – They are taking a genuine interest in what you are saying, are asking questions relevant to what you have said, and are thinking about you and your words.

Deep – They are taking more of an interest in you than themselves. They are visually and verbally engaged, they are completely focused on you, and they are able to accurately summarise what you have said. They at no point refer to themselves or advocate. There is unconditional acceptance of what you are saying.

Deep listening is exhausting. It requires conscious practice, focus and energy. It is not surprising that tired health professionals make poor decisions or are disengaged with patients. Their primary job is to listen and develop a comprehensive understanding of your reality. This takes energy, time and dedication.

With practise, you can develop your active and deep listening ability in social settings so that when you have to see a health professional you are equipped to get the best outcome for yourself. With deep listening you hear key words that need further exploration through asking building questions. You can use the 'Box Technique' explained shortly.

Why is listening important?

Quite simply, listening develops relationships as it shows you care about someone. Listening in itself is some of the best medicine you can ever give someone!

One question every GP or A&E doctor should ask every patient at the end of the consultation is: "Do you feel any better now compared to when you walked in?" Many patients with a non-urgent condition just want someone to talk to about how they feel. They are being listened to!

The reason therapy, group sessions, coaching, counselling and mentoring all work is because of one thing – conscious and structured **listening**. Listening is about giving and investing that most precious commodity of all to someone else – your **time**.

Taking the time to listen to each other is something that both you and your health professional should be doing in abundance for each other. It is a false economy to rush through a conversation just to hit a target. Many hours, funds and errors would be saved and avoided but for having a quality conversation in the first place.

The relevance of this to your healthcare is that not being good at listening can have dire consequences. What if your mind is so preoccupied with assumptions and yourself that you miss critical information? What if you go into a conversation with such a rigid agenda that you miss vital dialogue?

Other reasons we don't listen: (many of these reflect personal desire to be in control)

Selfishness – Wanting to talk about ourselves. Thinking about our opinions and experiences is somehow more important and valid than what the other person is saying.

Perceived time pressure – Jumping to conclusions too quickly and wanting to move on.

Agendas – Wanting to get our point across and being stubborn.

Boredom – Not being interested in what is being said.

Judgement – Rushing to conclusions because we think we already know.

Stress – Thinking you are too busy to put the time into listening.

Status – Thinking you don't have to listen because you are far too important to possibly learn and gain anything from someone else. Ego alert!

On a scale of 1-10, how good are you at genuinely listening? If you think you are good, what makes you a good listener? How many of your friends would describe you as a good listener? If you are not so good, identify your personal barriers to listening and think about how you may address them.

Of the healthcare professionals you have met, how many of them are a really good listener? Have they ever asked you for feedback?

Learn to listen – it could save your life.

How to practise listening in social settings:

★ Only talk about yourself or your own experiences if you are asked a direct question.
★ Don't respond to comments from others by starting a sentence with 'I'. Practise self**LESS**ness.

*   Practise by asking questions that build on each other.
*   If you are on the phone, don't do other things that take your attention away: reading web pages, writing emails, watching TV. Focus on what the person is saying – **give them your time.**

How to be a good listener:

1. Suspend your personal judgement
2. Don't interrupt others
3. Don't talk about yourself unless asked
4. Focus!
5. Ask questions that are relevant to what you have heard
6. Summarise what you have heard

Doing more of this will also endear you more to others, quickly and exponentially developing your relationships, and generally helping you to be a more respectable human being.

Summarising

(The act of repeating what you have heard with as few words as possible to clarify the meaning and understanding of what has just been said)

Through asking good questions and by practising conscious deep listening, you can use *summarising* as a technique to check your understanding of what you **think** you have heard.

Summarising in a healthcare setting helps you, the patient, and the professional in front of you to take stock of what has been said, to reflect on the conversation and to confirm the **facts.** Summarising the facts in hand is essential before making a decision about what to do with your body.

With medicine being a complex issue, it is easy to get lost in what has been said. Even in a simple setting in everyday life, it is very common for two people to have a conversation then walk away thinking they both have the same understanding of what the issues in hand are and what is about to happen – only for the reality to be something completely different! How many times have you either said or heard someone say, "Well I thought we were going to…!"?

A large part of this is the way we are hardwired to receive information. Some of us will focus and spend more time listening and remembering the details and facts, whereas some of us will be more able to remember the concepts and ideas. An idea to one person can be intent to another. Only through summarising and checking can you bridge this gap in understanding and avoid the unfortunate post-event wisdom of, "Well I thought we were going to…!"

You don't have to try to do anything clever or overtly smart with summarising. After a period of time, openly say something along the lines of, "I'd like to summarise my understanding to check we are in the same place…"

Once you have summarised your understanding, follow it up with a clear question,

"Is that what you said?"
"Is that a fair reflection of the facts?"
"Is there anything I have missed?"
"What else do I need to know?"

Part of the power of summarising is the concept of 'playback'. When we are talking we are on transmit, and few people have the ability to accurately recall and repeat what they have said verbatim. Playback is the idea of you, the patient, replaying what your healthcare worker has said to help them better understand what they think is going on and to achieve better accuracy. It's amazing how many people change what they have said when they have something played back to them verbatim!

Summarising cuts through the quantity of words, potential

confusion, opinions and guesswork to focus on the key salient points and facts that are the bases for making the best decisions.

It may help you to summarise by taking notes when you have a conversation, perhaps by writing down key words or phrases.

Another useful method is to **get a friend to do your summarising for you**. When you are worried and stressed and thinking you may be ill, it can be difficult to process a lot of information rationally and objectively. Ask a friend to listen and take notes to then summarise what they think the facts are. This can help ease the pressure on you and it can be useful to hear an observer's recollection of the conversation.

Summarising also allows the healthcare worker time to think about the conversation and add critical information as needed.

The importance of summarising:

* To establish the facts
* To achieve clarity
* To improve accuracy
* To check mutual understanding
* To help decision-making

A quality conversation between you, the patient, and the healthcare worker will involve both of you using summarising. The healthcare worker should use summarising to ascertain and fully understand your reality and history, and you should use it to check what you think is going on.

The better you are at listening, the more accurate you will be at summarising.

We are now going to introduce you to a visualisation technique that brings together all the skills we have covered so far.

The box technique.

This is a technique you can learn that will quickly help develop your listening skills and a deeper understanding of someone else's reality. It is an efficient way to find out what another person is thinking about and referring to when discussing a topic. Medical students have been taught this technique and found it very useful in allowing them to build rapport and understanding with patients much faster than a checklist approach to questioning.

As a patient, it's useful for you to know if the health professional is exploring your reality as deeply and thoroughly as possible. You can use this technique yourself to explore the key themes you have heard in any conversation. Building your own awareness of what is happening in a conversation will make you a more effective communicator.

How the box technique works:

Listen to the other person's opening statements in any conversation. Pick out two to four key words they have used. Then think of each of these words as a label on a box. You can't see inside this box. The other person, however, knows everything about this word, and their experiences, emotions and understanding about how much this word means to them. Explore this word with them by asking further questions to discover what you need to know and what the other person really wants or needs to share with you. Now check your understanding before 'opening the next box' and exploring that label. Each time, summarise and check. It takes much less time this way to get to what the other person and you, the listener, needs to know and share. This technique develops active listening skills and helps build rapport and mutual understanding.

Try the box technique and see what happens. Practice will sharpen your listening skills and help you discover new information.

Ears hear but we don't always listen. Let's look at real listening and practise with an exercise for you to try:

Ask a question to a friend or family member.

E.g. "What was your last holiday like?"

Then follow the guide below...

1. Listen to their response.
2. Listen very carefully to the words they use and pick out three significant words.
3. Now imagine these three words are labels on a box. You can't see inside the box but the person you are asking questions of knows and has experienced everything that is hidden from you in the box.
4. Now ask questions about each label (significant word). Begin these with *what, when, how* or simply, *"Tell me more about that."*
5. For each label (significant word), summarise back what you have heard.

You should have experienced a deep and thorough conversation that leaves you very aware of that person's experience on holiday. It may help to write down key words as you listen to the first answers. You could practise summarising back to see if the holiday you now describe sounds like the one they went on. This could be a new radio game show! You will hear some skilled interviewers use this technique on radio.

Next try asking about the last time they saw a healthcare professional and think about how the conversation went, how would it have been different if the box technique had been used and review how much information was shared and listened to. What examples do they have of the significant boxes being opened? Which critical boxes were left unopened?

There are two benefits to knowing about this technique when it comes to your care –

1. You will know whether the healthcare professional has actually listened to you and opened your boxes. If you have not done much talking and you leave the conversation feeling like you didn't get to say what you wanted to say, it's likely they didn't.
2. Once you have told the healthcare professional what is concerning you, there will be a conversation where they tell you some information. It is for you to listen intently and open the boxes of the key words that they use.

Next time you see a healthcare professional, listen out for the key words and open those boxes!

How to get the best outcome from every healthcare conversation.

THINK IT – SAY IT – CHECK IT – PLAN IT

Having learnt the fundamental skills of communication and how they can help you get better care, this simple framework will give a flow of how to lead a conversation and be in greater control.

A	B	C	D
Think it	**Say it**	**Check it**	**Plan it**
What are your concerns?	Clearly share your thoughts and concerns.	Has the healthcare professional listened and understood what you have said?	What have you decided?
What are all the symptoms, events and facts that you are thinking about?	How is this affecting your life? Express how worried you are.	Have your worries been addressed?	What is your plan of action?

If you practise the process opposite you will realise that effective communication is a combination of asking good questions, actively listening and then checking mutual understanding. The conversation needs to allow questioning between the people without the fear of being judged for asking a poor question, or the fear of being abused for asking a good one.

An example of the above process in action:

Think it – Consider the whole scenario. This is a general overview of what has been happening. What is the background? What symptoms have you had? How long have things been concerning you?

Say it – Sharing and expressing your reality. Now consider what specifically has troubled you the most and share this with the health professional. What is REALLY concerning you? Has it affected your lifestyle? What have you been doing about it?

Check it – Summarising and checking. Listen carefully to what the health professional says back to you and try to summarise your understanding. Open those boxes. Have your main concerns been addressed? Repeat them if needed and ask further questions.

Plan it – Making clear decisions. Based on what you have heard, what are you going to do now? How will you follow up? What have you decided to do that is in your best interests?

Why using this framework is so important:

Dealing with your emotional needs and addressing the facts is the way to improve your overall wellbeing. Your aim is to leave the conversation having had your worries listened to and then addressed. This simple framework, combined with your communication skills, will give you the ability to be in control.

Think of that last time you saw a health professional. How much of this framework did you use? What could you have done differently? Were your emotional needs met? Was the plan and outcome agreed, satisfactory and ultimately your decision?

Negative communication

We are occasionally on the receiving end of communication that closes down the dialogue negatively and blocks good communication, which in turn potentially affects our care.

There are many examples, such as no eye contact, no explanations of procedures, not answering questions and not explaining things as requested.

A recent example of poor/negative communication was a GP whose opening line was; *"I only have five minutes, what's wrong with you?"*

Whilst this time constraint may be true for him, it runs the risk of shutting down the patient who will then not open up. It could make the patient feel like they are bothering the doctor and that the doctor's time is more important than the patient's care.

Poor and negative communication should be directly challenged. A response to the above GP's comment may be, "Are you in the right frame of mind to be seeing patients? If you are unable to properly examine and diagnose me in the next five minutes, who can see me who has more time?"

Some may see this as confrontational! But remember – take control; IT'S YOUR BODY!

(Of course a conversation may only need 5 minutes if you both use good communication skills!)

Here are some other examples of statements we have personally heard from health professionals. It is not in your interests to simply accept negative dialogue – think about how to respond in a way that can help you. This list is by no means exhaustive but should give you a flavour to think about how you respond.

Negative communication and your possible responses

Health Professional statement	Your poor response	Your better response
This is not possible, I can't help you	Oh!	Please get me someone who can
Well that is just ridiculous	I am sorry	Please explain why
You are just being difficult	I am sorry	What is it that you find difficult?
We will just have to wait and see (often used when person doesn't know)	Ok	I'd like to discuss this with someone else
I don't have very much time	Oh sorry, I will go then	Let's agree a new time now
There is no evidence	Really? I thought there was	Do you have all the facts available? Let's review them together
Leave it to me	Ok	What, how and when are you getting back to me? What can I expect?
I'm just a locum	Oh I see	Are you checking your decisions with a senior doctor?

Communication skills summary

Why are good communication skills needed?

Many errors in interactions between people are down to poor

communication. Most of us assume we are good at communicating despite the fact that many of us have spent little or no time thinking about what it actually involves. More alarming is the fact that healthcare professionals, who would themselves mostly agree communication is a key skill in delivering excellent patient care, either have limited formal training or forget to use these skills. They are often stretched by hectic schedules making effective conscious communication difficult – but worse is being so deluded that they deny needing any extra help to improve. The great news is that the current generation of medical students now undergo communication skills training as a major part of their education.

The ultimate aim we seek is a conversation between two or more people with a free exchange of ideas and concerns and without the barriers of status, bias, misguided self-interest, delusion or the fear of ridicule and with facts being valued more than opinions. In this way the professional uses their skills and knowledge to address the concerns of the patient. Talking in this way allows the patient to maintain control and keep their needs clear. This approach overcomes a two-way assumption block. Such a block occurs when the healthcare professional assumes the patient will state their main concerns and the patient assumes the healthcare professional will ask the right questions and know all the answers. There are many barriers to achieving clear communication, not least from the patient's perspective is the fear of finding something is wrong and the possible need for treatment.

The skill of really listening, acknowledging and responding appropriately will go a long way to addressing the major concerns in the NHS during the last five years.

CHAPTER 9

Decision Making and Risk

How to make decisions and understanding the risks

After all that questioning and listening you now need to make a decision – often the most stressful part of any health-based interaction. It's time for reality…

Ultimately, **all decisions[10] that are going to affect you should be made by you,** the patient. In surgery, and many other areas of healthcare, this is known as *informed consent.* To help you achieve this, it is the job of the health professional to answer your questions, educate you, deal with your concerns, inform you of the options available and the relevant pros and cons. By gaining knowledge of the background to the critical elements of a conversation and by using the contents of this book, you will be in more control of what happens to your body and be able to make the decisions that are in your own best interests. When making a decision, you are of course assessing the associated **RISKS** which we explore shortly.

One of the reasons **you** should be making decisions is that at the literal end of the day, your healthcare worker goes home to their normal lives and you are still living with whatever it is you are worried about!

One of the most common questions asked of any healthcare worker is:

"What would you do if you were in my shoes?"

Answering this heavily loads your decision-making process and removes the impartiality a healthcare professional should have in decision-making.

There is only one person in your shoes – and that is you!

Your healthcare professional cannot possibly know everything that is going on in your mind. Nobody knows you better than you.

There are of course some medical conditions that may seem incredibly complex, making the prospect of fact-finding and making a decision daunting. The challenge for the health professional is to simplify the facts so you, the patient, fully understands.

Healthcare professional – educates
Patient – decides
Healthcare professional /Patient – implements

To really simplify the process, the doctor should educate, the patient should decide, and the implementation should be a dual responsibility. The patient follows the advice for taking medication, having physio and follow-up appointments, and the healthcare professional implements their side of the plan.

The irony in patients accepting the decision of a healthcare professional is the patient still has to sign a consent form – which is your signed declaration and decision to go ahead, accepting the risks. At least know what they are!

What you need in order to make a decision that's best for you:

* A full understanding of the facts
* Knowledge of what all of the options available to you are
* The pros, cons and **risks** of each option
* The likely or possible outcomes of each option
* The plan of action to implement the decision (Plan A)
* What will happen if plan A does not produce the desired results? (Plan B)

Discuss your decision with a friend or relative, explaining your rationale. If they are good at listening, they will ask you questions to help you realise if you have made the best decision for you at that moment.

Many of us don't like making decisions, whether it be where to go on holiday, whether to split up with a partner, what to do at the weekend, or whether to have surgery. We often ask the question of friends, *"What do you think I should do?"* If you go on a holiday that a friend said you should go on and you hate it, who do you blame? Some of you will blame yourself for listening, and many will turn the poor outcome on the friend and their suggestion!

The reason so many couples spend hours having the same inane conversation, "Well, let's just do what you want to do. Well, what do you want to do? Well, it's up to you, but what do you want to do...?" is because: *The one who decides holds responsibility – and where there is responsibility, there is blame!*

> *How many times in a restaurant have you ever said to the staff, "So what do you recommend, what's good?" A large part of this is not wanting to take the risk of being responsible for ending up with a dish that you are not happy with. It would be novel if you got the response, 'The soup is disgusting and the lasagne is a great bowl of tasteless sloppy mess'.*

A reluctance to take responsibility for our decisions is common. You can avoid getting into blame-based discussions if you invest the time establishing the facts in the first place. It is this lack of time investment that is singularly the biggest obstacle in making the best decision.

Rumination is the process of unduly dwelling on the past and wondering, "What if...?" What if you had made a different decision? Of course it's easy to be wise after the event as hindsight is the wisdom we all possess. There is no such thing as a wrong decision if you honestly believed it was the right thing to do at the time, as it's impossible to know if the other options would have produced a better result. Indecision is actually a decision – to do nothing!

Visit the NHS page on decision-making for additional help and guidance: they call it *shared decision-making* and can be found at www.sdm.rightcare.nhs.uk.

Ultimately you are the person who is going to put the drugs in your body or have someone operate on you.

No surgery is routine or minor – they all have the same risks!

These include: infection, bleeding, scarring, allergic reaction, error, incompetence, variability, failure and death.

or SUCCESS (mostly)

MAKE IT YOUR DECISION!

There may be some of you who just want to be told what you should do when you are ill. If that is what you want, then you should agree in writing that you have decided to take the healthcare professional's advice. They still have an overriding duty to put your best interests first. But do be mindful of being told **you need** to do something. Only rarely is 'need' unequivocal. You cannot reasonably expect to hold someone else responsible for the outcome if well-known side effects or risks occur and you decided not to be involved in making the decision on what options exist, having primarily already agreed and decided you do want your illness treated in some way.

The four questions you should ask before any course of treatment or surgery:

1. What's the best outcome I could hope for?
2. What's the worst outcome I could expect?
3. What's the most likely outcome?
4. What are the percentages of success for each option?

74

The plan you then make becomes a balance of probabilities – and RISK!

What is risk?

We all think about RISK in our everyday lives: driving a car, riding a bicycle or crossing a busy road. During each of these activities we assess our personal risk many times, sometimes without conscious thought.

In short, RISK means something MIGHT happen as a result of making a decision. That decision could be to consciously do something, or actually to do nothing. Of course many people forget that doing nothing is a decision in itself and therefore carries its own risk. For example, being in a hospital bed and lying still doing nothing has serious risk of developing a blood clot in the legs or worse, inside the lungs.

The something that might happen may be a **good** thing OR a **bad** thing. There may be multiple risks at the same time and so then we talk about a 'balance of risks'.

Health professionals like to talk about risk when discussing treatment and surgery. The health professional and the patients' understanding of risk can be very different. Risk is often poorly communicated and poorly understood. These mix-ups in communication about risk may lead to unexpected outcomes and subsequent complaints.

Risk does not mean **Causation**

Simply put

Playing the lottery even just once means there is a risk you might win. You know that almost certainly you will not, even if you play for your whole life.

Perhaps the most important thing to realise about risk is the fact that there is a risk DOES NOT in itself mean something will happen (Causation), or is likely to happen, or that it is only a matter of time before something will happen. Something may never happen, whatever the risk.

If your healthcare professional goes quickly into TELL mode, for example, *"I think you need to/should do…"*, it is unlikely they have assessed your risk preference, or have an awareness of their own risk behaviour.

Check! – Ask the question;

"Tell me how you have factored in my risk preference and any bias you may have towards this treatment?"

You may get a great clear answer or you may get a dismissive, "I know best", or even an angry, "how dare you" response! This should clearly help you decide if you want this healthcare professional to treat you.

Once you are happy you have a clear exchange of information that includes having your concerns fully discussed, and are happy you understand the pros and cons, you are now ready to make a plan of what happens next with your healthcare professional.

Further thoughts on RISK

Health professionals are used to talking with each other about the risk of prescribing drugs and carrying out surgery. They have studied books, read professional papers and attended multi-national meetings to discuss in detail many treatments and the risk of using them.

Health professionals use their risk judgements to decide what to treat you with and how successful they will likely be if they use a particular treatment. Their assessment and understanding of risk is often seen through the mirror of justifying their own professional knowledge and skill. This is risky – for you!

We are all prone to bias, misinterpretation, marketing and even misrepresentation. Every treatment potentially has a number of agendas behind it, which aren't necessarily best for the patient.

A question asked of health professionals at interview when discussing a medical service redesign or a particular treatment is: *"Who takes the risk when health professionals make decisions?"* The most common answer from the person being interviewed is *themselves* (the health professional). Surely it's the patient that takes the physical risk, first and foremost? This error in thinking is not uncommon if the health professional is primarily focused on themselves rather than the patient.

Medical treatment is of course not a one-dimensional risk assessment. If society becomes too litigious and everyone resorts to blaming health professionals for every poor outcome or error and there is a 'zero tolerance of error' then the risk is health professionals won't treat, surgeons will refuse to take on more risky cases and students will find other courses to study.

In other words, risk has to be looked at from everyone's perspective, but ultimately the patient should be put in the best position possible to make an informed decision on what the risk is to them.

A farmer listened to his surgeon explaining the overall risk of the procedure as being 1 in 1,000 for bleeding, 1 in 800 for infection, 1 in 2,000 for failure, etc. The farmer replied, *"Well, it's 50:50 then; it will either go well or it won't!"* leaving the surgeon somewhat perplexed. The farmer's perspective is very different to the surgeon's. The farmer, the patient, **takes the physical risk.**

RISK: Facts can be found, but how they affect you is unknown and can't be fully predicted.

Figure 7
Where does your healthcare worker keep this?
No healthcare professional can fully predict your future.

The healthcare professional often feels they are going to be affected by a treatment decision. However, the PATIENT is the one who deals with the benefit and/or the side effects, the discomfort or worse. Healthcare professionals may be psychologically affected by decisions but not by their physical effects. Some health professionals like to sound authoritative when discussing risk (this may make them feel justified and clever). The farmer neatly summarised that no one can know in advance what will happen.

So now some good news: most often in medicine, risks are small and the benefits far outweigh the risk of something going wrong. For example, modern cataract surgery is a very safe procedure. However, there is a 2% chance of a problem afterwards which will usually resolve quickly without visual impairment; however there is a small risk of about a 1 in 8,000 chance of total blindness in the operated eye. Most of us wouldn't accept even this small risk of harming our sight if we could already see perfectly well. Yet some people have cataract surgery before they have a cataract. They do this to reduce their need for glasses. Other people opt for laser eye surgery despite good vision with glasses or contact lenses. This shows we have individual risk perceptions and risk-taking behaviours.

Given that health professionals and we, the patients, both have our own risk perceptions and behaviours, how do we come to a decision for each treatment? The answer is once again through good communication and questioning and listening skills (SEE SKILLS SECTION).

Questions to ask your healthcare worker about risk

1. How often do you do/give this?
2. What are your results?
3. How many years' experience do you have?
4. How often has it not worked?
5. What do you do when it does not go right?
6. What is the worst case scenario?
7. What if I choose to thank you for your advice and do nothing?
8. How certain are you of these outcomes?
9. What would you advise your own parents?

Questions to ask yourself about risk

1. How would I feel/cope if this went wrong?
2. How does my choice affect me from both positive and negative outcomes?
3. Where do I think I fit on a line of 100% go ahead versus 0% not going ahead? (In other words, how comfortable am I with my decision?)

100%	Take the risk						Avoid the risk	0%

Assess your normal attitude to risk

For interest, you might like to assess your general risk behaviour and attitudes now, using the scale above again when engaged in the following activities:

* Driving a car
* Speeding in a car
* Flying in a commercial plane
* Riding a bicycle
* Horse riding
* Jumping off a diving board into a swimming pool
* Diving off rocks on holiday
* Drinking alcohol
* Smoking
* Taking banned drugs or substances
* Taking out a mortgage or loan
* Eating fatty foods
* Talking to strangers
* Trying new things

Think of other things you do regularly to better understand your attitude to risk.

Making your plan of action

Once you have a decision (based on your needs and risk analysis), you need a plan. **What, when, where, who?**

WHAT is going to happen?
WHEN will things happen?

WHERE will things happen?
WHO is implementing these things?
WHEN will we review progress?

Once this is discussed, shared and understood with the clear timeframes set out, you should also schedule and know when the reviews will take place.

Who on earth in their right mind would carry on implementing something that they know is going wrong and not stop, review, question and change to get a better outcome? Well shockingly in healthcare too many staff, and in life too many people!

Positional authority, seniority and the fear of repercussions are the main reasons staff do not question and challenge other staff during treatment and surgery when they think something is going wrong. Professional arrogance is the cause of many errors. Back to aviation: read up on the worst air disaster in history in Tenerife in 1977.[11]

Humans inherently have an *'attraction of action'* and generally feel better perceiving they are doing something, rather than doing nothing – even if that 'doing something' is wrong, inefficient, and not in others' best interests and even if doing nothing is stopping, reviewing and asking good questions. This behaviour comes from the very top in healthcare at a political level. How often do we hear opposition parties saying to the one in 'power', *"Oh, there they go again with another embarrassing U-turn."* Because surely it's better to just plod on doing the wrong thing to save face and reputation rather than stop and head in a better direction? What many people fundamentally fail to realise is that to admit that the direction they are heading in is wrong and they have to change plans is to be honest and human. Honesty builds trust and prevents further errors. This value-less culture permeates and corrupts the NHS and society in general.

A friend, who is a General in the British Army, said succinctly, "No plan survives the first bullet." To think you can just make a plan and then go blindly forward is folly. You and every healthcare worker connected with your care should be asking questions at every stage of your health journey to check and see if it's the best plan for you. Every politician, healthcare trust CEO and NHS manager needs to grasp the fact that pretending and attempting to be perfect is inhuman and impossible. It is this delusion that has led to the repeated lies and cover-ups that have cost people's lives.

"If plan A isn't working, let's try plan A and see how we get on with that plan."

Strange how it still isn't working?

The fundamental ethos of the people development training industry in corporations running team and leadership development workshops stem from what is known as *experiential learning*. That is, to learn from our experiences through reflection, we can learn how to behave and perform better in the future.

"What's working well, what's not going so well, and what could we do differently for a better outcome?" (The only three questions any coach, trainer or facilitator needs to learn!)

In the case of your healthcare and treatment, your review questions could be:

"What's working?"
"What is not working?"
"What do we need to do or change for a better outcome for me?"

Reviewing is a critical part of your healthcare journey, performed by yourself, your family, your friends and every healthcare worker you meet.

We will revisit this in the 'Your Health Journey' section.

Here is a summary of two approaches to doctor/patient communications:

Conventional Model of a Healthcare Professional/ Patient Interaction

★ Patient explains symptoms
★ Healthcare professional presents solution, often mainly assumption-based
★ Healthcare professional is the most important person in the room

In this, the 'old school' method, you gave the healthcare professional a brief history, they then made some best guess assumptions and sent you on your way. The healthcare professionals think they are pretty important. This still happens – but don't let it happen to you! It may be okay – but so many times things are missed, resulting in delay, developed illnesses, extra cost, uncertainty and stress.

Coaching Model of Healthcare Professional/Patient Interaction

★ Patient leads conversation and does most of the talking initially
★ Good questions are asked of each other
★ Mutual levels of listening
★ Facts are reviewed
★ Both check understanding
★ Rapport established
★ Summaries are shared
★ Decisions are made
★ Actions and plans are outlined
★ Clear next steps and review scheduled
★ Healthcare professional is of service to the patient

This model requires a much greater initial time investment – but will significantly minimise the chance of missed diagnosis, poor care and unnecessary stress.

YOUR HEALTH JOURNEY

We are now going to take you on a journey through the health system as you would experience it from starting at home, to seeing your GP and then going to hospital.

At each stage of your journey there are key questions to ask, summarising and listening to be done, followed by careful decision making. The prior skills section will help you prepare and manage each stage of your journey.

We suggest you use the skills and journey sections together to help you get the best possible care. We also recommend that you keep a written record of what you have learned about your illness and how you used your communication skills at each stage, what worked and what to ask/change next time.

Thinking slowly and carefully at each interaction throughout your health journey will help you develop and refine your communication skills.

Reflecting and acting upon what you noticed will help you get the best healthcare in the future.

One of the most effective things to do when you see any health professional is to take a trusted friend with you. *Before* you go, discuss your concerns, reasons for going, questions you would like to ask and what you would like as an outcome from the visit.

Ask your friend to take notes as you lead the discussion with the healthcare worker so you can review the conversation later and discuss your next steps. Before you leave the conversation, refer to your friend to ask them if you have missed anything.

CHAPTER 10

At Home

A nice place you don't want to leave – in an ambulance!

Figure 8
Am I ill?
A conversation that begins with you.

Self-delusion can often be your biggest problem. Ask yourself these three questions:

Am I ill?
Do I need medical help?
Have my vital signs changed? (See appendix)

The first step in realising that you may have a problem is to question yourself. Whether this be a thought inside your head, out loud, or into the mirror, they are all perfectly acceptable (as long as the mirror doesn't actually answer you back!). Journaling is a very powerful and useful process – write down your symptoms or thoughts to help address what is concerning you. How long has this been going on for and what is associated with the concern or worry? (Look at the 'Skills' chapters for more information.)

Then share this concern or worry with a family member or friend and find out more about it; explore what is happening to you and what you can do to stop this concern!

You may realise you are just fine and can carry on, but you also may need to take action.

Questions to ask yourself

Share your answers with friends and family to help you get more detail and formulate your next steps.

Main Questions	Following questions	Deeper action questions
What has changed?	★ Which part(s) of my body are affected? ★ What have I noticed?	★ When did this begin? ★ Which other parts of my body are affected? ★ Is this continuous or intermittent? ★ Is it getting worse?

How serious is this?	★ Have I stopped doing things? ★ Am I avoiding things? ★ Have I lost weight unexpectedly?	★ Will this get better by itself or do I need help? ★ What might happen if things continue or get worse? ★ Am I still worried having checked?
How do I feel?	★ How worried am I? ★ Rate this 1 to 10	★ Who shall I tell or share my concerns with? ★ (1 is slightly concerned; 10 is extremely concerned)
What knowledge do I have?	★ Where can I get information?	★ Do I need professional help? ★ Can I sort this out myself?
How much time before I do something?	★ How long should I wait? ★ How long have I had this?	★ Can I treat this myself? ★ When am I going to get help? ★ Ask family, when did I first mention this?

Now DO something! – Don't think that by just asking questions and even sharing concerns that you have already taken enough action.

A failure to act when you genuinely think there is something wrong with you is delusional. It is also well-known in psychology that the mere thought or act of saying you are going to do something can lead you to believe you have already acted sufficiently to fulfil your intentions. (One of the many reasons diets and New Year's resolutions do not work – "I am going to lose weight" etc…)

Prepare your story – *Before seeing a health professional*

This is the key part of how you begin to communicate either to your GP, to an on-call health worker by telephone, or in person at Accident and Emergency.

Include only what is truly relevant! (Don't include random information such as details of the last time you went to Bognor on holiday, or what Auntie Ethel said about dinner whilst watching *Strictly Come Dancing* last Saturday). A little ritual conversation may help ease your nerves but very few GPs will have the time for it.

Use this framework to prepare your story:

1. Noticed – What have you noticed – when did you notice it, for how long, what are the signs and symptoms?
2. Changes – What different, physical changes are there? Are there any other changes (emotional, etc)?
2. Time – How long have you been experiencing this? How often does it happen? This is critical.
3. Effects – What are the effects on your daily routine and work?
4. Concerns – What are you really worried about? What are the key questions you REALLY want answers to?

Knowledge – tell the healthcare worker what you have heard, read and researched.

If you turn up to see your GP having prepared using this framework they will like you a lot! We know this as this model is what many have told us is how they wish every patient would communicate with them.

NOW WRITE DOWN YOUR:

PERSONAL IMPACT STATEMENT 1
What is your story?

Your personal impact statement is what you need to have prepared for when you visit either your GP – or if it's more serious, Accident and Emergency. It should contain accurate and concise information based on your answers to the questions in *preparing your story*.

You must be honest with yourself and avoid denial and delusion. As an example:

A family member thought that exercise was the best way to get rid of the progressively worsening abdominal pain. After three days of sit ups and stretching to get rid of the 'trapped wind', now in severe pain, a trip to A&E took place and his infected appendix was removed that day, just in time before it burst!

Many ways exist to get information at this stage. The internet is now an incredible resource for health related concerns. You can of course very quickly convince yourself you have most of the symptoms listed for a particular condition as so many are typical: lethargy, headaches, nausea etc… You have to try as best as possible to be honest with yourself. It can be great to discuss your concerns with family and friends to get good advice and be persuaded to act early. We often don't remember what we have already told those close to us.

Basic checks of body function you can do at home

If you do these regularly, over time you will have some idea what is normal for you

* If you have a thermometer, take your temperature.
* Use a minute timer and check your heart rate. Are the beats regular?
* If you have a blood pressure machine, check your readings.
* Have you been to the toilet as you normally do? Was it your normal colour?
* If you have a blood sugar testing device, check your level.
* Have you lost weight unexpectedly?

If several of the above have noticeably changed, you should be seeking further medical help.

If you do need to go to hospital because you are feeling unwell, the above list of vital signs and checks is how the hospital will assess you. If you already have a record of how you have been over previous days or weeks, this could be very helpful and allow a quicker assessment to diagnose what may be going on for you. Illness can be defined as changes in what is normal for you.

What is 'normal' for me?

Most vital sign checks and other bodily tests produce figures and a range of variation. What is low for one person may be normal for someone else.

If you do wish to undertake a self assessment of what is normal for you, you will need to check your vital signs in a systematic, routine way. (e.g. weekly at the same time, on the same day and at rest.)

Your GP will not need a weekly update on changes *within your normal variation!*

In the future, devices are likely to exist which will monitor our body's function and download the information to our home computers and smart phones continuously if we wish. We will then get a message when we need to seek professional advice or help.

CHAPTER 11

With your GP

Are you making the most of their time?

Figure 9
'How government targets help your GP listen to you.'

Good general practitioners are worth their weight in penicillin. Laughter however, it is said, is the best medicine... unless you have syphilis in which case use penicillin.

Your First Visit

You have had some time to think things through. Now it's time to go and see your GP. Have you got your story ready? Have you thought through what your *real* anxiety and fears are? Have you got your key questions ready? Make sure you use the time available with the GP wisely (approximately ten minutes) and get what you need from your visit.

How often have you left the GP and thought, "I am none the wiser", "I didn't really get the answers I needed" and "I am still worried"? Did you give the information that you were concerned about? Did you ask the right questions? Did your GP listen to your worries?

To help you avoid leaving the GP none the wiser read this section.

Start simple and then get into more complex discussion if you wish. Starting with a longwinded and loaded question may stifle your GP's ability to think freely to address your real needs. Reference the Patient Communication Process in the 'Communication Skills' section earlier in the book.

How to make the GP interaction work for both of you

Why would you think your GP has not listened to you or dismissed symptoms? This communication breakdown happens too often. The 'Skills' section of the book is there to help you become a better communicator. GPs want you to get better quickly so you can go home and live your life in a healthy, happy way. Occasionally, patients need to be referred to specialist care in hospitals. Your GP only wants to do that if it is really required.

GPs get ill too, so let's not be one-sided about illness and stress. Happiness and health are to be shared. A survey of 500 GPs in the UK found that 72% were emotionally exhausted, 41% were depersonalised and 97% felt they were not achieving a great deal.[12]

Additionally, 80% of GPs said they fear they might miss a serious condition in a patient because of their intense workload pressure.[13] It would seem many GPs are stressed, unhappy, time-pressured, heavily criticised and **need your help**.

Helping your GP

It is not a yes/no game! Your GP is not a mind-reader, magician, mystic or psychic. They need your help to be able to help you. A good story (history) usually leads to a more accurate diagnosis and helps your GP consider other possibilities. Prepare you concerns and symptom story carefully and clearly (your personal impact statement 1).

Having spoken to many GPs, their dream patients are the ones who communicate their medical history clearly and succinctly. Have your story prepared!

Seeing a GP for the first time

If things go well, then it should go something like this:

The 10 steps to seeing your GP.

Use your personal impact statement as a guide and refer to the Communication Skills section to Question, Listen, Decide and Plan.

1. Hello Doctor. Thanks for seeing me. You look well/tired/harassed/ great *(build empathy!)*
2. This is my story…
3. This is what I am worried about…
4. Your GP should then ask you 2 key questions:
   i) What do you already know?
   ii) What would you like to know?

5. How confident are you in the main diagnosis? How much do you know about this condition? Please tell me more.

Listen carefully to your GP's answer, then ask the GP appropriate probing questions if needed. (Refer to the 'Questioning skills' section.)

6. What else might it be?
7. What is the treatment/side effects?
8. How will I know if it is working? How quickly should it work?
9. What do I do if it gets worse?
10. Who do I contact?

We have heard numerous patient stories of GPs saying to them, "So what would you like me to do for you today?" This is an attempt to get patients to take some responsibility and open up the conversation but is not quite the right question. Many patients have said it's just annoying! There is an obvious and short answer – "I'm ill, make me better!"

This is an example of all too frequent and poor quality conversation between a patient and a GP.

A great question for you to ask...

From the patient to the doctor:

> *"What would you do if you were treating your own mother?"*
> In others words, what is the best possible care they can give
> (assuming they love her!).

If all has gone well, and often it will do, you will be satisfied, reassured, have a clear plan and know what to do next.

If things did not go so well, then perhaps something like these **real** examples happened:

A. The patient was interrupted quickly by the GP saying, "I don't have time" or "I only have five minutes". The patient was then put off and thought, "Well, I had better not raise my concern fully", and played down their worries so as not to waste time. This meant the patient left more uncertain, annoyed and uninformed, resulting in a delay of another two weeks and the need for yet another appointment. They might have said, "I understand you have a time limitation, however I'm very concerned about my health and would like to see someone who has the time to discuss this with me thoroughly. Who else can see me today?"

B. The patient was talked at for five minutes but heard and understood little, was not listened to, could not understand much of what was said, and felt increasingly worried. They perhaps might have said, "That was very thorough but somewhat complicated, and I didn't understand much of that. Can we check what my main concern was?" They would then have found out what the GP thought was their main concern, and have had a more useful conversation.

In A) the GP is blatantly not doing their job (i.e. "I'm not prepared to see you") and in B) the GP is trying to blind you with science and words using ego and status. It can be very difficult as a patient when you are confronted with behaviour like this. The important thing to do is remain calm and ask the questions you need answering – or ask to see someone else.

C. The patient went in to the clinic feeling guilty about wasting the Doctor's time and only went because family members made her go. She didn't prepare her full story and failed to explain all her symptoms. She was prescribed anti-depressants for a headache and sore face. She got them from the pharmacy then refused to take them – labelling the GP as an idiot in the process!

This probably happens dozens of times every day across the country and wastes a huge amount of resources in time, energy and costs. The GP didn't attempt to take a proper history as the patient was not forthcoming and he was perhaps feeling pressured to at least do something! There were some huge assumptions on his part in deciding that anti-depressants were the solution to the symptoms. You can avoid assumption based decisions and get the best care by following the guidelines to communication in this book.

Once you have been to see your GP, write down your reflections of the experience as your **Personal Impact Statement 2.**

PERSONAL IMPACT STATEMENT 2
A reflection on how you now feel.

What do you now know?
Are you worried? If so what about?
Have you got clarity?
Are you happy?
What do you wish you had said or asked?
What do you need to do next?

Getting access to your test results

Depending on your symptoms you may be asked to undertake tests to try and detect abnormalities that can be found in things such as blood tests or biopsies. Many of us will expect a phone call should something worrying show up in the tests. This unfortunately does not always happen as we would expect.

Don't assume that because you hear nothing about your test results that it means everything is ok. The tests may have been lost or actually be abnormal and not acted upon. *'No news is good news'* does not apply to your test results!

ALWAYS follow-up with your GP after having had any tests done. Be pro-active: ask what the results were, and ask for copies to keep for your own records. Take some action to share the responsibility for your care. You will hopefully hear that things were 'normal'. As we have already said, they need to be normal for you.

Your second visit to your GP

You may need a repeat visit because you are not getting better.

At this stage, you should ideally be seeing **the same GP** as on your first visit, to maintain context and consistency, and in order to develop rapport with them. Unless, that is, you have serious doubts about their performance on your first visit and want a second opinion; in which case ask to see someone else.

Actions and questions for your second or further subsequent visit

Review your **Personal Impact Statements** – write another one answering the same questions and compare your answers. Much of medicine is based on observing and acting on *changes* in your health over an observed time period.

For example, a standalone measurement of a red blood cell count for one person may be 'normal' and within the 'nominal range', yet for another it may be outside the 'nominal range' and yet still be 'normal' for them. It is only when you are able to compare changes to signs, symptoms and measurements that a clearer picture of your state of health may be deduced.

When you re-visit your GP:

1. Repeat your symptoms and anything NEW or WORSE. Share what has changed. Have a quality conversation as described previously.

If you get referred or feel that you need further investigation:

2. Who do I need to see now?
3. What might happen next?
4. How do I prepare for that?
5. What help can I get; who, when, where?
6. Who is the best specialist in this area of illness?

With a bit of good fortune and the great ability of the body to heal, you will get better and the next step won't ever happen, but if it does, you may be going to hospital.

CHAPTER 12

Going to Hospital

Figure 10
Going to Hospital can be a scary experience.
Who is waiting to help you?

Your journey continues…

Your GP may have tried to treat you with medication and/or performed blood or other tests. If your health concerns have not been resolved they may say that you need specialist help, which invariably means you need to go to hospital. It is a notable step up from having a casual walk to see your GP. Hospitals are often big and busy, and can give you a feeling of great uncertainty as to what will happen next.

You will have days, weeks or perhaps months to gather your thoughts, reflect on what has been said so far, check your understanding and prepare for your hospital visit. Given the media coverage, it is likely you will have heard many things said about NHS hospitals, much of it very negative. Your challenge is to focus on what your real concerns are and share anything new that has happened since you last saw a doctor. Use the time with the staff you meet as efficiently and as usefully as possible by being well prepared.

To prepare for your hospital visit, go back to your story and add to it as needed.

Use the same framework as when you were preparing to see your GP.

Framing your story

1. **Noticed** – What have you noticed – when did you notice it, for how long, what are the signs and symptoms?
2. **Changes** – What's different, what physical changes are there? Are there any other changes?
3. **Time** – How long have you been experiencing this? How often does it happen?
4. **Effects** – What are the effects on your daily routine and work?
5. **Concerns** – What are you really worried about? What are the key questions you REALLY want answers to?

By preparing your story well and when a good specialist asks you those same 2 key questions, you will be in a great place to be able to answer them.

1. **What do you already know?**
2. **What would you like to know?**

> Stay in control of your experience
>
> Ask lots of questions
>
> Listen carefully and summarise when required
>
> Leave more informed with an agreed plan

CHAPTER 13

Hospital Outpatients and A&E

Making it less scary

Figure 11
Use your waiting time to prepare for a quality conversation.

Outpatients

Welcome to outpatients – long waits, read a book, hope there is something good on TV. Why are they showing personal injury lawyer adverts on a loop? Thank goodness there is a decent coffee shop in the foyer. You are telling me you don't have my notes again? The specialist isn't here? Why have I waited four hours to be told I am not seeing anyone? An all too frequent outpatient experience.

It doesn't have to be this way. Many outpatient departments are run very well and are pleasant, efficient and put you at ease. Indeed, managers like to focus on appearance whilst being able to do little about the clinical service quality. They are busy places and time is precious. Most people will have waited longer than they hoped, so we can all help each other by preparing beforehand. The patient who turns up and opens with, *"Well, you are the doctor, tell me what is wrong with me"* is not really helping.

Have you prepared for your visit?

Below is a table to give you some ideas about preparing for your visit. Go through the table and think through who you will be meeting and what you will want to know.

Good questions

Event	Basic questions	Deeper questions
Getting what you want from the clinic receptionist	★ When I am likely to be seen?	★ Who am I seeing today? ★ Am I seeing a senior doctor today?
Speaking with the clinic nurse	★ What can you tell me that might help me today? ★ Is this an area you fully understand? ★ How sure are you of this/that? ★ Who would you want to see in this clinic?	★ What will happen next and when? ★ What is the doctor like? ★ Would you let this doctor treat your family? ★ Are they running late? ★ How do they like information? ★ Will I be able to ask questions?
Seeing your specialist doctor for the first time	★ Has my GP's letter been helpful? ★ Do you have my previous records and notes? ★ What were your thoughts after seeing my referral notes?	★ How confident are you in this diagnosis? ★ How will I know the treatment is working? ★ How long will this take to work? ★ What are the other possibilities? ★ What are the risks?

Seeing the Specialist

Take some responsibility and do some **preparation**. Don't assume your GP or referrer has communicated everything that is important about you. Time will have passed since you were referred, perhaps months have gone by and you may have new things wrong or new feelings or concerns. So, once again – prepare! (We keep saying that to remind ourselves to do it). You have a lot of time to get ready so make the most of your time with the specialist.

Firstly – review your personal impact statements – remember honesty and openness as this is the culture we are building together. Create a new Personal Impact Statement 3, which is an up to date summary of your worries and highlights what you would like as an outcome.

Secondly – use your communication skills and the THINK IT – SAY IT – CHECK IT – PLAN IT framework.

Listen to what the health professional has said to you and summarise what you have heard so far. When you feel comfortable enough to do so, move on to decision-making and agree a plan together.

Refer to the 'Skills' chapters earlier. As you are potentially making bigger decisions about treatment and/or surgery, make sure you are also referring to the chapter on risk.

You might find that all this happens seamlessly without you having to think through the guidance above. Many doctors and healthcare professionals have had advanced communication training, have invested time improving their own communication skills and so are capable of putting you at ease immediately. They may have answered almost all of your questions and addressed your concerns within a few minutes. Such health professionals are usually experienced but more importantly have compassion, patience, humility and high levels of awareness. That is great – every patient should expect a similar service. In contrast, being told up front not to ask questions or being told you have limited time, or even largely ignored and talked at, suggests the individual you are with needs help with their ability to do their job.

After seeing a specialist, there will invariably be a decision made and a plan of action put in place. Reference the skills section for help in this process.

In summary – get all the FACTS to help YOU make the best decision for yourself. Know what the plan is and what part both you and the specialist will play.

Seeing a Healthcare Specialist

* List what you have heard about your symptoms or condition.
* Decide how much you would like to know from the specialist: most details/just the overview/as little as possible about your condition.
* Be very open and honest if you feel comfortable. For example, tell the specialist why you are frightened or concerned about specific things.
* Let the specialist know how much time each day, week or month you have spent thinking about your condition.
* Ask the specialist to tell you what to expect next.
* Ask with whom and when you can make contact within the hospital team if you need more help later.

Your plan for what happens next

Remember it is your body we are discussing; it is up to you what happens next, so be involved and in control of the plan as much as you want to be.

When you walk out of the consulting room you will know whether you feel that the experience has been positive and if you are in control. If you are walking away from the outpatients department puzzled, confused, alarmed or so angry that you won't be going back, then clearly things did not go well. Given the healthcare professional is there to help you, something has gone sadly wrong. Were your expectations too high? Did you voice them? Were you listened to? A good consultation usually means a clear two-way communication happened. Hopefully you and the healthcare professional both listened, questioned, checked understanding, summarised and ended with a clear plan. This may mean further tests, another check-up, or that a drug or operation is needed.

The authors know of senior professionals who don't believe they need help communicating effectively and think that as their time is precious and short, there is no time to let the patient speak beyond stating their basic symptoms. The irony of course is that it saves huge amounts of time when effective communication is allowed as it leads to quicker diagnosis, builds rapport and understanding, prevents complaints, and above all, prevents error and harm. The consequences of poor communication result in much more time being used and resources wasted.

Refer to the 'Skills' and 'Communication' chapters. Think through and rehearse questions that you might then ask of the health professionals you meet at the hospital. Practise makes perfect. For example, if you are thinking you may need surgery, good questions to a surgeon may include, "What are the most common complications you have with this operation and how do you deal with them?" "What are your outcomes?" Such questions will tell you a lot about your surgeon.

Visiting Accident & Emergency

Occasionally you will have to use an Accident and Emergency department if you have a sudden health concern or accident. You can still use all of the skills we have covered to help you get the best possible care. In the worst case scenario, you may be accompanying

Figure 12
A&E – Have you really had an accident or an emergency?

a friend or relative who is not in a position to communicate for themselves. You can still ask all the relevant questions and follow the processes suggested to help them get the best possible care.

A&E services have received a huge amount of press coverage in the last few years. The issues range from cuts, unit closures, pressure on services, waiting times and ambulance delays.

Let us all agree one thing: being able to pitch up anytime day or night, 365 days a year and get free medical advice and treatment, is simply a huge privilege and an amazing benefit compared to health systems across the world. Given the fact that it is so fundamentally important to our society, why do so many people turn up and abuse it, either utterly out of control due to alcohol, abusive, ranting, threatening and often hurt through self inflicted injury or with utterly trivial minor ailments?

ACCIDENT AND EMERGENCY is the name. It is not is a walk-in centre or convenient alternative GP service. There are GP and nurse services set up to deal with extra non A&E cases. Many hospitals do have GP primary care services set up alongside A&E to help deal with the excessive demand. Your area may have a walk-in centre for non A&E concerns.

The demand on A&E is huge: over twenty million patient visits a year! That is the equivalent of a third of the UK population visiting once a year. Or are the same 55,000 accident-prone people visiting daily? Of course, all of these patients don't form an orderly queue and turn up at regular intervals. This means A&E can be extremely busy dealing with horrific injuries and other life-threatening diseases with a finite number of staff. Reviewing such acute care and opting to design service provision based on mean numbers results in woeful under-capacity at times of greatest need, and staff being much less busy at other times. Slack time can be used for training and necessary administration and review, not as an argument to reduce staffing levels further. Overcapacity in complex urgent services is a good thing. To go back to aircraft, or indeed the human body itself, huge overcapacity is built in to allow for stresses and variation so things keep working well even under stress.

So, given all this pressure and finite resources, think through carefully your options when you are feeling unwell. Your first action should **not** be: "Oh, the GP is closed or booked up, I will just go to A&E." Go back to the chapter 'At Home' and work through your check questions, check your vital signs, check with family or friends, and then decide what a rational action is. You might save yourself a five-hour wait and help others get faster care. Clearly, if you are genuinely acutely or suddenly ill, ring 999 or 111 for help and advice.

Once you do arrive in A&E the communication skills you are learning by reading this book will serve you well in getting the help you need. They won't change your condition directly, but they will help you get better, more efficient care.

CHAPTER 14

Being in Hospital *(including operations)*

How can you influence your care?

Figure 13
Are you getting the best care?

Being on a hospital ward

Being admitted to a hospital ward can be a scary and lonely time. It means something is wrong and further investigation and treatment is needed. After the initial shock of the admission process, there is often a feeling of loneliness, isolation and boredom. Things happen slowly, lots of people go by, and few people have the time to speak to you. Everyone is 'busy'. You may find you spend more time talking with the cleaners, healthcare assistants, charity workers, tea ladies and medical students than any senior health worker such as a qualified nurse or doctor. When the doctors and nurses do appear, it's often quickly, without warning, and briefly!

Somehow you need to stay in control and understand and participate in your care. Unknown to you, there will be masses of paperwork explaining all the detailed care you have been receiving from the nursing teams to 'legally' document that your 'care pathway', 'care plan', or whatever the local jargon is, has been followed. You may have spoken to or seen your 'designated nurse' or 'carer' on one shift, but not again. Announced in June 2014, you are even going to have the name of your specialist written down in bold to emphasise who they are, so they are reminded that they are responsible for your overall care.

How to ensure your 'care plan' is about you:

1. Have your vital signs been recorded regularly?
2. Have you been to the toilet in your typical pattern? (No.2s)
3. Have you had enough to drink? Are you passing urine ok? Are you well hydrated?
4. Are you in pain? Has your pain score been recorded? If in pain, what has been done about it? You are aiming for zero pain.
5. Are you too hot/cold or just comfortable?
6. Have your levels of uncertainty been dealt with?
7. Which doctors and nurses are you going to see and when – on a daily basis?
8. Do you know what is happening next and when?
9. Are you being turned or having DVT treatment if immobile?

How to ensure better care in hospital for your relatives

Visit often and take an interest in what is happening and what is planned, learn the names of the staff on the ward, help out if possible and help each other. Ask lots of questions about their care, what is happening and how to offer support and help.

If you have a relative or friend that works in healthcare, there can be some benefits to mentioning this and sharing what you discussed about diagnosis and possible treatment. It can often just take a small trigger to put into action a whole different course of investigation or treatment.

If care appears poor, ask to speak with a senior nurse and consultant. Make sure you have thought through what you need to know and what points you want to make. Instead of a rant or emotional outburst of dismay and anger (however well justified), try to get the nurse and consultant to state what the acceptable standards are and whether these are being met. In other words, set out what the minimum standard is under their care. Put your concerns and observations into the form of a question. For example, instead of, "My mother has been left without food and drink for twelve hours!" ask, "What is the maximum time for an elderly bed-bound patient to go without food and drink on this ward?" Demand a specific answer. Clearly, this has been breached or you wouldn't be asking the question. Now you need to find out who had the responsibility on the day in question, what is being done, who has been held accountable, who is going to see the improvement occur, and what will happen if this occurs again. If this conversation is a series of answers that dismiss and trivialise your concerns, then demand for your relative to be moved to another team of carers. Raising it with your MP can have a dramatic positive influence. Not all politicians are useless!

If many of us reasonably challenge poor standards and ensure those responsible are held accountable then slowly the culture can change. Nurses sat in offices with huge files and reams of paperwork aren't caring; they are justifying the political process that strangles the NHS.

An important question to ask everyone you meet in hospital looking after you:

"WHAT IS MY NAME?"

We all forget the names of people we know. We find it hard to remember the names of people we have recently met for the first time. We don't usually remember the names of strangers we meet briefly. Yet crucially, your name (and number) is how carers know that you are the correct person to receive a drug or an operation. People make assumptions and errors often – we all do. Check that each new person about to treat you knows who you are and that the right treatment is being given. This will help stop or reduce a preventable error. One of the most common errors in hospitals is patients either been given the wrong drugs or the wrong dose.

To reduce error, one of the best dialogues a nurse can have with you is as follows:

1. What drugs are you expecting us to give you?
2. What effect are you hoping it will have?
3. Are you aware of the possible side effects?

If the nurse does not ask you these questions – you should be asking these questions to them!

Prescribing paracetamol or changing a drip may be seen as 'routine'. But remember, there is nothing routine about putting any drugs into your body. Be in control and know exactly what is happening and why. As we have stated in the communication skills section, having open and transparent conversations is a major step in getting better care and reducing error and harm.

This is not just another check list. By having an open conversation and a two way dialogue, you are first getting more clarity and certainty as a patient, and secondly helping the staff reduce avoidable error.

A campaign called *'Hello My Name Is'*, has been running for a number of years.[14] Started by a doctor receiving cancer treatment, she noticed how few healthcare workers actually introduced themselves before giving treatment or advice. If you don't know the name of the person treating you – ASK! Putting a name to an action generates responsibility in any setting.

Operation Time

Figure 14
Managers and politicians improving the quality, safety and efficiency of surgery

If your health gets to the stage where you need a procedure in the operating theatre, there are a number of things you can do to remain in control and get the best possible care.

Modern surgery has developed and progressed to levels

thought impossible thirty years ago. Depending on the type of surgery, you may be fully awake with local anaesthetic, sedated but relaxed and forgetful, or under general anaesthetic and completely asleep, unaware of what is happening. Many procedures have options for the type of anaesthetic used; discuss with your surgeon what is available and what your preference is.

Things are getting safer in operating theatres, but we have not eliminated all error and harm.

The recently introduced World Health Organisation surgical safety checklist has been brought into operating theatres. It has already shown it can reduce error and improve teamwork, communication and outcomes; which is good when it is used in the spirit as intended.

HOWEVER!

The risk of any checklist is that it becomes routine to the team repeatedly using it. Read up on the controversy around care of the dying in the *Liverpool Care Pathway*.[15]

Moreover, using a checklist itself can become the primary aim, not the actual thinking through of what matters to the patient lying there about to be operated on.

> RR – *In my own theatre I had a frightening experience that reinforced just how quickly human behaviour defaults to 'I am using the process, so I no longer have to think for myself.'*
>
> *A nurse continued to SHOUT the steps of the checklist across the theatre with absolutely no self-awareness of the needs of the patient, so loudly in fact that I couldn't hear the patient talking. This was on an operating list where every operation was the same, all the equipment was the same, and the same eye was being operated on in each patient. Indeed, the only real risk of error was that of making sure the correct size lens was used; a crucial check the nursing hierarchy had refused to implement*

meaningfully for six years. During which the wrong lens had been used four times due to a variety of errors not addressed by the checklist.

This real story above highlights how an imposed checklist implemented in a robotic way overrides genuine clinical safety. Generic checklists can create a culture *devoid of responsibility and accountability as behaviours are geared towards checking the checklist and not the patient's needs!*

A routine checklist may rapidly become meaningless

Consider this:

The one person who is in the operating room or the anaesthetic room who really does have a huge level of interest and thinks this is far from routine is you, the patient.

If you have already been fully anaesthetised you are most definitely not involved in the pre-operation final check. A recent discussion with a young man revealed he overheard the staff routinely checking final consent to remove both his testicles, when in fact it was only one testicle to be removed! He had the awareness and confidence to make sure the staff knew it was one-sided removal. This was far from routine for him.

Read on to start thinking about how to look after yourself and help the staff break their 'routine'. Today you are a special case; let them know you are.

Routine surgery

No surgery is 'routine' in reality, however minor. Every case has its own peculiarities and risk factors. Most surgery results in a good outcome.

However, all surgical procedures and surgeons have complications. The surgeon who claims never to have had a complication belongs to one of three groups: i) they have not operated on enough cases, ii) they are lying and denying their complications, or iii) they have a very selective memory. The truth is of course that good surgeons recognise, deal with and admit their surgical complications quickly, and still achieve good results usually.

The five questions you should ask before accepting a surgical procedure:

1. What's the best outcome I could hope for?
2. What's the worst outcome I could expect?
3. What's the most likely outcome?
4. What are the percentages for each of those scenarios?
5. What are the outcomes of the complications you experience as a surgeon?

The plan you then make becomes a balance of probabilities and risk. Re-read the chapter on decision making and risk.

JUST BEFORE ENTERING THE OPERATING THEATRE

Be fully involved in the final checks!
If you can, ask these questions of the
OPERATING SURGEON

Which operation are you planning to do?
On which organ/part of my body?
On which side?
What outcome can I hope for?

Do this immediately before entering the operating room if possible. Make sure you are happy the staff know what they are doing.

DO NOT ASSUME!
Do not hand over control of your body until you are happy.

If the surgeon can't see you just before surgery, they should have definitely seen you on the day of your operation to discuss it with you.

They should PERSONALLY mark you with a pen where the operation is to take place.

We know of one surgeon who uses a smiley face rather than an X or arrow – to make things a little less traumatic for the patient and more personal to him.

Always ask, who is going to perform the surgery? If you are having a complex procedure with multiple staff, ask who will be responsible for what.

It would be of great reassurance to see the surgeon who will operate on you immediately before you receive your anesthetic. It may have been hours since you saw them and they may have operated on numerous patients in the interim.

It is common for medical students or other healthcare staff to observe operations. You should ask who else will be in the theatre and in the interests of education, suggest they be part of all conversations regarding your surgery – so they understand the whole picture.

They might just notice something if the main surgeon makes an error.

If the staff are having an off day, they may be distracted by other human factors: events, crises, bureaucracy, targets, personal fall outs, etc. Make sure they are focused on what **you need** before the surgery starts.

The comparison of checklists in the aviation industry is worth considering. The pilot and co-pilot will go through the pre-flight checklist with the full knowledge that any error won't just affect their passengers. If every healthcare worker (and manager) involved in your care suffered the same level of discomfort or consequences as you do when something goes wrong, we suspect that standards of care and checklists would improve exponentially!

You may be worried that questioning the team may interrupt their happy day and the easy-going, calm atmosphere. When people are in too much of an easy-going comfortable mode, you get complacency. Complacency means people are more likely to miss things and make errors. Having people on their guard, attentive and actively concerned is a good thing.

WHEN THINGS
GO WRONG

This part of the book is hard to read, hard to believe and even harder to be in such a situation when something has gone wrong. It is when your communication skills will be truly tested and your ability to ask great (and challenging) questions will be critical in you getting the truthful answers that you deserve.

If enough of us persist in getting the truth and demand that those in positions of responsibility are held fully accountable for their actions, then perhaps the NHS can become a much safer and transparent organisation.

CHAPTER 15

How Complaints are dealt with in Hospital

Figure 15
How are your concerns and complaints dealt with?

Illness by definition means things aren't going well for you. Many diseases are controllable, only some are curable. The role of the health professional is to keep you informed and comfortable, and relieve as much physical and mental stress or discomfort as possible. Modern hospitals have lots of ways of investigating you, medicating you and operating on you, but it is how they treat you and make you feel as a person that you remember after each episode. What far too many patients have experienced, and what has now gained increasing exposure, is how they are made to feel when they have needed to – or, some say, had the audacity to – make a complaint. Complaints may simply be an enquiry as to why things didn't go as well as expected (did you ask the right questions?) or may be a very real observation or experience of poor care, error, neglect and harm. Figures suggest there are 3,000 complaints about the NHS daily, half of which are about doctors.

Let us start by reminding ourselves that hospitals do amazing work in diverse situations, dealing with everything from in-grown toenails to severe trauma or cancer care. Many things are fairly routine but some are extremely complex and challenging.

Things do go wrong, will go wrong and might still go wrong in the future. But we should learn from error, and reduce further errors by being open and transparent, and not having a default position of *denial first*.

No one in his or her right mind sets out to make an error or deliberately cause harm

Definitions of ERROR and HARM

There are a number of definitions of Error and Harm. The most commonly used in the media is that Error is: **an unintentional mistake or mishap committed unconsciously that leads to Harm** (physical or emotional injury).

The second definition of Harm is that it is: **an act of wilful negligence, deliberate oversight or malicious intent carried out consciously or an act without full consent.**

Another word used to describe the second definition of harm is malpractice.

Whilst accepting that errors occur, we all hope, assume and expect hospital teams to learn from them, reflect and share learning, and be completely transparent so to prevent future problems from the same errors. Improving the way complaints are dealt with will go a great way to help bring about the open, honest, transparent culture we all need. Ann Clwyd MP has published a review of NHS complaint handling following her own horrific experiences.[16]

Unfortunately, the evidence is that learning from complaints is not happening at it should be

Given that error and harm are occurring and not being sufficiently learnt from, the obvious questions are:

★   Why? How do we know when an avoidable error has occurred or has been repeated? How do we know that past lessons have or haven't been learnt from? Who is responsible? Why would denial, cover-up and lies be used to cause further harm and distress to an already upset and vulnerable person?

★   Why would the most extraordinary errors result in the highest levels of secrecy?

The assumption that our complaints and concerns are learnt from and shared widely is just that… an assumption. Let's look at what happens to complaints in a typical hospital.

Each hospital has a **team of people whose job is solely to answer complaints,** which is in itself a worrying reality. These are known as 'patient liaison' or 'customer care teams'. Many complaints are about administrative errors, missed appointments, wrong addresses or delayed follow-up. Some complaints are frivolous, such as commentary on the decor and perceived attitudes in busy, stressful, overbooked clinics with struggling courteous staff doing their best.

However, genuine complaints about poor care or communication are not uncommon. Delayed treatment, wrong diagnoses, mis-information, wrong treatment and poor outcomes also feature.

This current culture, at its heart, is all too often about avoiding blame, avoiding admission of liability, avoiding financial pay-out and above all avoiding bad publicity. This has been highlighted in numerous news articles.

The huge irony is that with an honest and transparent approach, error and harm would be highlighted immediately, preventing further error. Those at the top would then be able to reflect on their great leadership and improving safety record!

This hasn't been happening because of the insidious management culture of 'don't bring me problems, only good news stories'. This is coupled with a reluctance to deal with individuals and poor performance due to legal frighteners (staff who are challenged often resort to claims of harassment, human rights infringements, racial or sexual discrimination etc.) All too often the common response to dealing with serious concerns is; "It's very difficult" (Jargon for, *"I am not going to do anything."*).

Hospitals are political places run by managers, not clinicians, who often have precarious job security. Even a Chief Executive is a glorified middle manager that sits between the workforce and the Department of Health who set the targets. Marketing, image, public relations, and meeting political targets have been the priority for too long. All this comes from the top – government. This culture has got in the way of quality and clinician-led services that seek improvement in patient care in a transparent way which would reduce errors and therefore complaints.

Process and targets put first means people and behaviours come second

If you have followed the horrific accounts of cover ups and lies detailed in the UK press in recent years, you will be only too aware of the issues around how complaints are dealt with.

Let's look at the complaint process in detail and the various steps:

STEP 1

The overriding need of any NHS facility is to avoid legal proceedings and the protection of their image and reputation. This usually means the first response to a complaint is a carefully worded apology without admitting full liability, but apologising for any emotional harm or misunderstanding. This letter will have been collated by a patient liaison person, often an ex-nurse, secretary or junior manager, from statements taken from doctors and nurses involved or named in the complaint. Their combined responses with a chronology (timeline) will form the hospital response to your complaint.

In summary:

* Apologise and acknowledge distress.
* Explanation may or may not deal with concern itself.
* Often long, verbose and full of repeat apologies for not communicating clearly at the time of the error and for any misunderstandings.

This letter is signed by the Chief Executive (who may not have read it).

STEP 2

The second phase is an even more carefully worded response with some extra facts to address on-going concerns, and seeks to answer further questions you have raised. This response may offer some clouding and ambiguity of the clinical picture aiming to admit awareness of the complexity, again avoiding overall responsibility, accountability or liability. It will usually again express sincere apologies for misunderstandings and delays.

This letter is signed by the Chief Executive (who still may not have read it).

STEP 3

There then follows a tightening of response and a message to seek external review if this response is not satisfactory. You will be given numbers and addresses to contact.

You may be invited to discuss your concerns with members of the team to address any misunderstandings.

You will need access to notes so you can fully report your concerns and complaint to external regulatory bodies for an in-depth response.

If you still feel unhappy then you will be offered guidance on how to take things further with the Parliamentary Ombudsman.

After going through the three steps above, summarising the typical pattern, you may have been satisfied with the answers given or if something very upsetting has occurred or you suspect harm or serious error, you will very probably have more questions than answers and feel more concerned, confused and, quite likely, upset and/or angry now.

It is quite likely that if something has gone badly wrong you may feel like you have been fobbed off. Almost certainly you have been.

What to do next?

Go on a mission to get all of the FACTS and the TRUTH

1. Obtain **all** the medical records (often needs a written request).
2. Ask for **all** email correspondence VERBATIM (not summaries) from the trust/hospital about the complaint and care.
3. Seek two fully independent reviews of the case/complaint/concern (from a different county or part of UK).
4. Keep a personal record of all communications and dialogue with dates and names.
5. Keep in touch with the trust/hospital and make sure there is on-going care.

This can be arranged as required with another healthcare team within the hospital if possible, or nearby to the patient and/or carers as available if preferable.

6. If things have escalated further without a satisfactory outcome you may be offered recompense for damages if appropriate, without full admission of guilt or liability.
7. If you remain unhappy you may contact a solicitor or lawyer with the aim of going to court to agree how much is reasonable for the damages incurred and to seek the truth behind events. A word of caution here – this may be very expensive, go on for many years, you may never get to the truth, you may feel increasingly bitter and angry, and at the end of the whole process you may have a judge rule that no award is to be made or that no proof of lack of care occurred. Most cases never get this far, thankfully.
8. You may have had a successful review by the Parliamentary Ombudsman who may have found in your favour following their own 'expert' review. The Ombudsman will have instructed the trust or hospital to award significant and reasonable damages.

What is interesting in all this process is that usually at no point has any liability been admitted by the hospital or healthcare professional involved, and no action, re-training or professional body review taken place with any individual. Nor will there have been any attempt to look wider at an individual's performance and behaviour, or past complaints. Patterns are not looked for. Far too many things are looked at in isolation to seek rapid closure. There is a lack of willingness to put together a comprehensive review of any individual's pattern of behaviour or ability. Such an approach in the case of a poor performer would often lead to clear, consistent evidence supporting poor performance, which would highlight the previous lack of accountability in those responsible for that individual.

Any reasonable individual would want to learn to be better, not strongly deny their involvement, dismiss concerns and be allowed to carry on. Eventually, the worst offenders are removed from professional registers by the national regulatory bodies, but typically only after decades of on-going poor performance at many patients' sufferance. Is that really acceptable?

The organisation concerned will eventually admit error if instructed to do so by the ombudsman. However, this is an admission of process error; it will do nothing to address the cultural and organisational issues behind a failure, nor will it change any individual behaviour or look at human factors or fallibility.

As we have witnessed in the media in the last few years especially, every attempt is made to minimise positive change and instead maintain the status quo by rapidly 'moving forward', which is jargon for *forget and avoid responsibility*.

What can you do to improve the culture of how complaints are handled and seek the TRUTH quickly?

Ask these questions and demand detailed answers:

* What changes have happened to the doctor/nurse/health professional who made the error?

- ★ How many previous complaints have there been about the individual?
- ★ Have they, or other members of the team/department made the same errors before?
- ★ Have they made *similar* sorts of errors before?
- ★ What action was taken the last time?
- ★ What does their 360 appraisal reveal about their performance?
- ★ Was this 360 extensive? i.e. all the team, or narrow with only a few chosen individuals?

If all this is not forthcoming then suspect a cover up!

You may note that all these questions are about INDIVIDUALS and their performance. Remember that whilst many errors are due to processes, it is the *individual* who makes the actual errors.

We all make errors. It becomes a concern when the same errors are repeated by the same individual, team or organisation.

CHAPTER 16

How to Get to the Truth

Truth, trust and time

Figure 16
The consequences of cover ups

For too many people in authority, **truth** is an uncomfortable word. This has been exposed in the media over the last few years in many organisations including banking, politics, football and the NHS. Certainly in the NHS, it would appear that at last there is momentum to unearth all that has happened rather than continue to deny or distract from the truth of catastrophes in at least fourteen hospitals in the UK. However yet more uncomfortable and heart-breaking news is likely to follow. As we write this book we see the media covering issues around breast screening errors detailing unnecessary treatment, the Liverpool 'care of dying pathway' being used without care or compassion, Savile stories continuing to be uncovered, Mid Staffs hospital reports, Morecombe Bay CQC concerns, and yet more hospitals such as North Lincoln and Basildon reported as failing. A lot of work needs to be done to reveal the full extent of what is wrong in the NHS and ensure a cultural shift in behaviour.

Not only is it a worry that there has to be a policy on telling the truth, but a government sponsored consultation exercise to *decide* on whether to have what they call a *'Duty of Candour'*. i.e. "Shall we decide to tell the truth?"

By suggesting there needs to be a policy of *'Candour'* means there is an admission that the current culture is one that features insincerity, evasiveness, and dishonesty.

Question: Why avoid the truth?

Answer: It is uncomfortable, it means taking responsibility for a decision or an action, it makes you accountable and you will be judged by others.

A lesson every decent parent almost certainly instils when bringing up children is to ask them to tell the truth. However, experience may inform us very early on that in doing so the result is that we don't get what we want. It is therefore, an ingrained behaviour not to tell the truth at first.

Wise parents will reward when the truth is told or take appropriate action as required when it is not, and will always emphasise the positive aspect of truth telling.

When you have done something wrong your inherent instinct is survival. Survival instinct is a short term action to get the safest immediate outcome for you.

If you have done something wrong, you should then tell the truth in order to maintain trust. By denying it, you have covered up the truth and when you are eventually found out, you will no longer be trusted. In effect you have harmed the person twice, once by your actions and once by your lack of integrity; no way to build a positive relationship – in any walk of life.[17] Trust takes years to build and moments to lose.

Was it a high minded idealist who decided to call hospitals 'trusts', or someone with a sick sense of humour?

No one benefits in the long-term from deception, cover-ups and lies. Time is usually a great revealer, as we have seen in many walks of life in the UK over recent years.

"I never have to remember anything, as I always tell the truth."

The hardest thing is not saying sorry – it is not even telling the truth – it is hearing the truth and doing something positive about it!

To arrive at the truth we need FACTS. Facts are not negotiable or open to interpretation. Facts exist in their own right and represent the truth. Facts have nothing to do with consensus, majority or convenience.

It is also important to realise that a consensus against or the convenience of ignoring facts does not change their existence; nor does the passage of time.

A very common tactic in the NHS is to use time as an excuse to ignore facts, knowledge and wisdom.

How is time used?

1. The crisis management and reputational management culture commonly says, "Well, that episode was **in the past** so it is no longer relevant today." The desire to deny that past events have relevance and may result in learning and prevention of error is typically reinforced by the phrase "we are looking forward and making things better". To live in denial and have voluntary amnesia may be a comfort but it is a false one, and a harmful delusion to those who suffer the consequences.

If we all took that approach to life, it would be like everyone having total amnesia and each and every one of us repeating the same mistakes every day whilst deceiving ourselves we have just done something new, exciting and useful.

2. Time is also used to **DELAY**. If you have raised a concern or complaint it is likely you feel awkward and guilty that you have questioned your care. You might even be assuming you have misunderstood or have been ungrateful. This mind-set is used to delay response in the hope your doubt will mean you give up on your search for the truth. We have seen in the media that it took over five years to uncover the Mid-Staffordshire truth and without that little or none of the additional truth would have come out about yet more hospitals. In individual cases delays go on for years before the truth finally emerges.

The lesson is DO NOT GIVE UP until you are satisfied you have the truth.

TIP: SET YOUR OWN DEADLINES FOR RESPONSES

Summary of Questions for Truth

WHEN?
WHO?
WHAT?
HOW?
WHY?

Researching as much as possible about a topic beforehand is also crucial. Be knowledgeable. Keep probing with simple questions until you are satisfied. Below is the sequence of events that can typically occur.

Cover-ups exist when there is a wilful intent to avoid the truth being exposed. Those who lie and cover-up the truth should face criminal charges. Many patients have suffered who simply should not have done so.

The anatomy of a cover-up

1. Deny any error.
2. Deny any harm.
3. Hold a meeting.
4. Seek to blame anything and everything bar yourself.
5. Find reasons not to do something about the issue.
6. Excuse the error/harm event as a communication error or misunderstanding/one-off (and then do nothing about it).
7. Under no circumstances tell all the individuals who were affected.
8. Do not alert or discuss with any external independent body.
9. Threaten staff with confidentially clause (now illegal but intent remains).
10. Forget it ever happened – "Oh it's just historical, we have moved on now."
11. Make sure the individuals who have 'whistle-blown' (told the truth), have their reputation and credibility destroyed.

It is worth noting that by this pattern of behaviour nothing is learnt, no one is held accountable, errors are repeated, performance and ability are never challenged and patients are kept in the dark about error and harm. The only outcome is that the corrupt system continues unchallenged, unknown and no person harmed *"is any the wiser"*. (*Laurel and Hardy – only this is far from funny*).

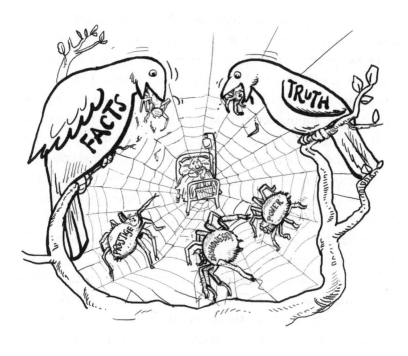

Figure 17
Patients need the truth

SUMMARY

We hope you have learnt things about the National Health Service that will open your eyes to the importance of acquiring and improving your own communication skills. The most important thing we can all do is to think deeper and longer to find the right questions to ask, and listen actively before summarising and checking our mutual understanding. This takes effort, and like any skill, takes time and practise to get good at doing it.

The alternative is to continue with the hopeful and optimistic assumption that politicians and people in power do their jobs accurately, honestly, consistently and avoiding bias and self-interest. History and reality suggest that this task is far too difficult. Too many professionals like the title and the salary, but not the responsibility and accountability that come with it.

We can together use our power as a herd to change the culture of our health service, and possibly wider society, by challenging authority with good questions and demanding better truthful answers. We all need to become skilled at highlighting the behaviours of avoidance, cover-up, harm and lies. With the internet, social media and rapid communications, spreading knowledge is now incredibly fast and easy. Almost any fact can be checked quickly. We all must be on our guard to ensure the accuracy of the information we discover and avoid falling into the trap of accepting the first answer that fits.

The role of health professionals is changing; our future as patients will see increasing use of technology and computer intelligence used to assist diagnosis, treatment, surgery and even decision-making. However, we as humans can focus on improving our communication skills and the clarity of information we seek. We can also help each other understand our emotional and preprogrammed evolutionary responses to risk and the possible outcomes of how our decisions interface with new technologies.

The key message from this book is that it is really up to you personally to do as much as you can to look after yourself. Ask good questions of those tasked with caring for you and your family. Set high expectations, challenge poor behaviour and performance, whilst acknowledging and sharing experiences of good care, so we all know where and who this comes from.

YOU can be one of the people who positively changes the NHS for the benefit of us all.

APPENDIX

ABOUT THE AUTHORS

Dr. Ray Radford MBChB MRCP FRCOphth
Consultant NHS surgeon and NHS patient

Ray has worked as a doctor in the NHS since 1990, following qualification in medicine at the University of Manchester. He had experience working in general medicine and haematology before training to become an ophthalmic, oculoplastic and orbital surgeon. Ray also taught and trained junior doctors and medical students in his position as Senior Honorary Lecturer at the University of Manchester.

Ray has been a patient of the NHS on frequent occasions. That he is alive to co-author this book is testament to all that is good about the NHS. His survival is part luck, part insight and in no small way due to understanding how to question people in order to maintain control over his own health as far as possible. His contribution to this book reflects his insights and personal experiences of the NHS. He shares this with you so that you too may benefit should illness befall you or your family.

"I was motivated to co-author this book following years of continued frustration working in the NHS, an organisation which can do such good yet still has a culture where the best are often ignored or side-lined. Skills and resources are so often wasted and at the same time poor performance is ignored, denied, or worse still covered up in the full and clear knowledge that it is wrong to do so; often done to simply save face or to avoid making real and difficult decisions for

fear of the truth and perceived legal costs. I resigned from my full time role to save my own sanity (and health!) and to allow me to deliver better care for NHS patients in the independent (private) sector.

I sincerely hope this book helps everyone make healthcare friendlier, individualised, of high quality, patient-focused and above all, safe."

www.DrRay.co.uk

Scotty Johnson
Founder of Yela!
Facilitator, Coach, Expedition Leader

Scotty has spent the majority of his life working with groups of people, helping them to learn, develop and flourish. He is the founder of *Yela!*, an organisation that provides opportunities for people to have profound learning experiences that help them live more fulfilling lives.

He works as a facilitator and coach with numerous multi-national organisations, business schools and charities running team and leadership events. His work recently has focused on developing personal mastery and improving personal well-being for a range of clients.

Scotty has had an extraordinary career; he was nearly thrown over the side of a ship in the South China Sea by his first boss, has lived in tents in the Arctic for eighteen months running learning expeditions, has helped international sports teams develop cohesiveness, has run yoga retreats from yachts in the Caribbean and has facilitated journeys in the desert to help people develop cultural understanding.

His motivation for co-authoring this book combines his passion for helping people to learn so they can make a real difference to their own and others' lives, and from his personal success using his skills and knowledge to get the best possible care as an NHS patient.

"Too often we look to blame others for our lack of success, health and happiness. We should first look to ourselves to see what we can do to improve our own lives through learning skills and developing self-awareness. This can be done through the power of reflection, questions and personal leadership. Practicing what we have shared in the skills section of this book will help you on that journey."
www.yela.me

Many thanks to Robin Grenville Evans for his brilliant interpretation and drawings of our ideas.

VITAL SIGNS

What are vital signs? These are your basic bodily function indicators. You could consider them like the speedo, fuel gauge and temperature gauge in a car. They tell you the current state of the machine. It is the *changes* in your vital signs that can give you an indication if you are unwell.

Here is a list of vital signs that you can check at home. Measure your vital signs regularly (at rest) and you will begin to understand what is **normal** for you.

Basic Vital Signs

Blood pressure
Heart rate
Temperature
Breathing rate

Additional Vital Signs

Oxygen saturation
Alertness
Urine production
Bowel movement (not a real vital sign but what's regular for you is *normal* for you, so has it changed?)

The following is a summary of the 'normal' ranges and values for the average **Adult** and is a simplified guide. For further reading and for a breakdown by age and vital sign, search the internet for 'Vital Signs Tables'.

Readings will vary depending on: you as an individual, your age, what you have been doing, the time of day and with temperature; what part of the body you take the reading from (mouth, armpit etc.).

Blood Pressure	90-140 mmHg (Systolic)	60-90 mmHg (Diastolic)
Heart Rate	60-100 beats per minute	
Temperature	36.1c – 37.2c (97F-99F)	
Breathing Rate	12-20 breaths per minute	
Oxygen Saturation	95-100%	

If you become ill, your vital signs will change. Dramatic changes in more than one of your vital signs may mean you are very ill and should be seeking urgent medical help or be in hospital quickly.

A sample of vital sign changes that are serious when feeling unwell (not a complete list)

* High blood pressure with slowing heart rate
* Low blood pressure with quickening heart rate and weak pulse
* Temperature over 39c with changes in other vital signs
* Failure to produce 1,000ml of urine in 24 hours
* Low breathing rate and reduced responsiveness
* Fast breathing rate with inability or reduced ability to speak, e.g. asthmatics

WHAT HAS THE NHS EVER DONE FOR US?

Top things the NHS has achieved since its introduction in 1948

FREE access for all.

NO additional cost (after tax) for advice, help, care, treatment and surgery in hospitals.

Subsidised drugs costs in the community.

Increase of approximately ten years in life expectancy.

Improved hospital and GP services with 24-hour availability for all.

Major breakthroughs

Treatment of infectious diseases with antibiotics.

Vaccination programmes against polio, measles, mumps, rubella, diphtheria, tetanus etc.

Cataract surgery – development of intraocular lens replacement.

Transplant organ donation programmes – kidney, cornea, heart, lung, liver.

Cardiac surgery – angioplasty, coronary artery bypass, pacemakers.

Endoscopic surgery with quicker recovery times.

Increased survival from many cancers, especially testicular and leukaemias.

Faster diagnosis and better accuracy with scanners, imaging software and computer assistance.

IVF and fertility enhancement.

Understanding of DNA and genetics.

Antiviral treatments for herpes, hepatitis and HIV.

Improved services for babies and children.

and much more...

QUICK REFERENCE GUIDES

Skills Summary

Questioning

Use questions that will give you the **answers** you seek
Use **OPEN** and **CLOSED** questions as appropriate
Use **building** questions that gain a **depth** of understanding

Listening

Keep your mouth closed and your **ears** open!
Give unconditional **focus** to what is being said
Listen for the key words that you need to **explore** (open the boxes!)

Summarising

Repeat what you have heard
Share what you understand to be the **facts** and **reality**
Check **mutual** understanding

Deciding

Understand all the **options**
Know what all the **risks** and **pros/cons** are
Be clear what **you** are going to do

VISITING A HEALTHCARE PROFESSIONAL

A	B	C	D
Think it	**Say it**	**Check it**	**Plan it**
What are your concerns?	Clearly share your thoughts and concerns.	Has the healthcare professional listened and understood what you have said?	What have you decided?
What are all the symptoms, events and facts that you are thinking about?	How is this affecting your life? Express how worried you are.	Have your worries been addressed?	What is your plan of action?

Prepare for your visit – what's your story?
What do you **really** want to know?
Ask **good** questions that are **short and clear**
Ask **open** questions to seek information
Ask **closed** questions to seek clarity
Use **why?** as a question sparingly
Consider **taking someone** with you, let them ask questions and
get them to take **notes** for review later
Get all the **facts**
Use **scale** based questions to develop understanding
Make the decisions **your decisions**
Understand the **risks**
Understand the **plan** and next steps
Make your own **impact statement** after every event/visit
Be in **control** of your body
Do the **follow up** – seek **results**
REVIEW

NOTES

1   31.08.12 Telegraph Newspaper. http://www.telegraph.co.uk/news/
    health/news/9508900/One-in-five-patients-harmed-in-some-hospi
    tals-data.html

2   21.06.13 Guardian Newspaper. http://www.theguardian.com/politics
    /2013/jun/21/jeremy-hunt-nhs-errors-patients

3   08.05.15 Independent Newspaper. http://www.independent.co.uk/
    life-style/health-and-families/health-news/health-secretary-jeremy-
    hunt-orders-annual-review-of-avoidable-deaths-in-nhs-hospitals-10
    0315 28.html

4   26.03.14 https://www.gov.uk/government/news/halving-avoidable-
    harm-and-saving-up-to-6000-lives

5   01.03.15 Telegraph Newspaper. http://www.telegraph.co.uk/news/
    health/news/11442029/NHS-bosses-to-be-criticised-in-Morecambe-
    Bay-mother-and-baby-deaths-report.html

6   Harvard Business Review 07.06.10. BP's Tony Hayward and the
    Failure of Leadership Accountability https://hbr.org/2010/06/bps-
    tony-hayward-and-the-failu.html

7   NHS Website. http://www.nhs.uk/NHSEngland/thenhs/about/Pages/
    nhscoreprinciples.aspx

8   David Beaty, 1995, *The Naked Pilot*, Airlife Publishing, Marlborough

9   Daniel Kahneman, 2011, '*Fast and Slow Thinking*', Allen Lane

10 There are of course people who, for a variety of reasons, cannot make
    informed decisions themselves. That, however, does not stop a friend
    or relative asking the right questions to get enough information, or
    seeking and using advocacy services. Two or more doctors acting
    together are allowed, where no capacity to make a rational decision
    exists, to make decisions on behalf of such patients. In difficult
    circumstances legal structures are involved and a *Lasting Power of
    Attorney* may be appointed.

11 Human Factors: Tenerife Revisited, Journal of Air Transportation World Wide Vol. 3 No.1 1998 http://ntl.bts.gov/lib/7000/75 00/7585/jatww3-1wilson.pdf

12 Pulse Today Website 04.06.13 http://www.pulsetoday.co.uk/ home/battling-burnout/revealed-half-of-gps-at-high-risk-of-burnout /20003157.article#.VU8Q_OvXIrg

13 Pulse Today Website 12.05.14 http://www.pulsetoday.co.uk/your-practice/working-life/80-of-gps-fear-workload-pressure-will-make-t hem-miss-serious-conditions/20006676.article#.VU8SwuvXIrg

14 02.02.15 Telegraph Newspaper. http://www.telegraph.co.uk/news /nhs/11383678/Dr-Kate-Grangers-Hello-my-name-is...-campaign-backed-by-400000-NHS-staff.html

15 16.07.13 http://www.theguardian.com/commentisfree/2013/jul/16/ dying-liverpool-care-pathway

16 18.11.13 http://www.theguardian.com/healthcare-network/2013/nov /18/hospital-complaints-review-ann-clwyd-trusts-comply

17 Ref: http://www.huffingtonpost.com/russell-c-smith/the-truth-about -lying-rei_b_2658951.html
Russell C. Smith
Huffington Post. 14 April 2013